EXERCISE SECRETS FOR DRAMATICALLY IMPROVING YOUR GOLF GAME

By

Michael Romatowski and Dr. L. Neil King

First printing 1998
Printed and bound in the United States of America

Published by Pierpoint-Martin
A Division of Gaucas, Inc.
419 Main Street Suite 47A
Huntington Beach CA 92648

This publication is sold with the understanding that neither the publisher nor the authors are engaged in rendering medical advice. Consult your physician before beginning any diet and/or exercise program. The programs described in this publication are intended for use by healthy individuals who have received a physician's clearance to exercise and are undertaken at your own risk.

ISBN: 0-889337-00-5
Library of Congress Catalog Card Number: 97-76113

AUTHORS AND WRITERS

Michael Romatowski

Dr. Neil King

Michael Romatowski is the founder and director of Super-Power Sports and Fitness, Inc. As a fitness consultant, personal trainer, and fitness writer he has prescribed exercise programs for hundreds of trainees, clients, and athletes. Michael is a graduate of the University of South Carolina, where he earned his bachelor's degree in journalism. He has authored several exercise books, including *Five-Star Fitness for Men,* and *Weekend Warrior.*

Dr. Neil King is a chiropractor and sports medicine practitioner in Montgomery County, Maryland. An avid golfer, he is also a competitive distance runner. Dr. King numbers many golfers among his patients and specializes in helping them rehabilitate golf-related injuries.

Thomas Stevenson, contributor to chapter 6, "The Power Golf Swing," is the head golf professional at Hell's Point Golf Club in Virginia Beach, Va. He is a lifelong bodybuilder and remains active both in competitive golf and weightlifting.

Dedication

This book is dedicated to:

Mike, who lives and golfs by the credo we both learned one day in the pro shop at the University of New Mexico Championship course. "Boys," drawled the female pro behind the counter, "If it ain't the U.S. Open, then don't bother playing it safe." Mike never does.

Kurt, who likes to grab difficult golf courses by the throat and shake birdies out of them like a pit bull shaking a rag doll. The harder the course, the better he plays; that's the mark of a true competitor.

Steve, the only guy I know who can win a match by nailing a 70-foot downhiller with 6 feet of break in a driving rainstorm, and make it all seem like just another putt. Also, the only guy I've ever seen who could (literally) make par from out of a graveyard, then gripe because his wedge shot from 100 yards didn't fall in for birdie.

Rich, who's "slashing" style seemingly allows him direct access to my bank account. His "short" game always leaves me "short" of cash by the end of the day.

You guys are what the game is all about.

Michael Romatowski

To my sons **Neil** and **Woody,** who, with their never-ending stream of consciousness-raising inquiries, have brought a freshness to my life and to my golf game.

Neil King

TABLE OF CONTENTS

Introduction By Michael Romatowski

October, 1993. I was standing in the eighth fairway at Tanoan Country Club in Albuquerque, New Mexico. The grass was greener than green, the sky bluer than blue, the sun shining bright, and my friend Mike Leahan's golf ball lay perched in a perfect fairway lie, a couple hundred yards from the lazily waving flagstick.

"Two-oh-four, downhill, away from the mountains, into the breeze, over the bunker," he mused. "What do you think?" We looked at each other and both said, "Four iron." He selected his weapon, strode confidently up to his ball, took his stance, and swung.

There was no mistaking the sound, that solid THWACK! that comes only from a ball hit dead-center on a fast-moving clubface. The ball rose into the air, so high it must surely have been picked up on the radar screens at nearby Kirtland Air Force Base. Then down, down, down it came, burrowing into the green a scant six feet from the pin. There was a moment of silence as we both admired the majesty of the shot. It was true power golf, and there's nothing like the feeling.

I want to play golf in a certain way: with maximum power. I want to smash the ball straight and far off the tee and wallop my irons right at the pin. I'm sure many of you seek that feeling of power, too. Strenuous physical training, especially weight training, can help all of us achieve great power. A physically strong person has an advantage in any sport, and that includes golf.

This book is about developing a more powerful golf swing by developing a more powerful body. The golf swing is an athletic move, similar in many ways to a baseball player's swing, a tennis player's forehand stroke, or even a boxer's punch. Any athletic move can and will be enhanced by an increase in muscular power, the combination of strength and speed. The goal of this book is to teach you how to develop overall muscular strength, then to apply that strength with maximum speed and precision in your golf swing. The result will be shots that fly longer and straighter. Male or female, young or old, all golfers benefit from added power.

First, you will learn about weight training. You will discover which weight training exercises are best for developing overall body strength. Second, you will learn how to strengthen the midsection, which may be the most important link in the "power chain." Third, you will be presented with a stretching program designed to increase overall body flexibility so that you will still be playing in your later years. Fourth, you will learn how to arrange an exercise program and a year-round training routine which combines all of the aforementioned factors in a logical manner. This exercise blueprint will answer all your questions regarding the frequency, intensity, and logistics of your physical training regimen.

Common golf-related injuries will also be discussed. Certain types of injuries seem to plague golfers, especially those in the "middle-age," and "senior" categories. A stronger muscular structure provides added insurance that injuries of any type are less likely to occur.

Finally, a PGA professional will show you how to execute a powerful golf swing. He will also advise you on how to practice for power, and how a Super Power Golfer attacks a golf course. A powerful body, powerful swing, and powerful attitude all go hand in hand.

Here's hoping you remain strong and healthy enough to play golf for many years to come. A lifetime of heroic "super power" shots awaits you. Condition yourself physically, then go for the glory every chance you get!

Foreword By Thomas Stevenson

I began playing golf in 1966 at the age of 12 after spending two summers as a caddy at my hometown country club. Golf was addictive. I played and practiced every chance I got, and at the age of 17 could consistently score in the low 80's.

That winter, I became more concerned about my appearance. At six-foot-three and 150 pounds, I was extremely skinny, and determined to do something about it. At the time, it was assumed that lifting weights would make a golfer musclebound; golfers never trained with weights.

Despite warnings that weight training would ruin my golf swing, I joined a gym and started training. I eagerly read the muscle magazines, and put the routines to use in my own workouts. By spring I was thrilled; my strength had increased dramatically, and I had gained more than 40 pounds of muscle.

When the golf season began, I was worried that my weight training regimen might have ruined my game. After work on the first day of the season, I teed it up, alone, just in case. A couple of practice swings felt okay, so I went ahead and swatted one off the first tee. It was the longest shot I had ever hit! I quickly discovered that weight training had not ruined my swing; instead, it had added 20 yards to my shots.

By the end of the season my handicap was down to 4; the following year I passed the PGA's Playing Ability Test and turned professional. In 1976 I made it to the semi-finals of the National Long Driving Contest. I have continued to combine golf and bodybuilding. I am convinced that a properly applied weight training program can dramatically improve one's game; it has certainly done so for me and many of my students.

1: Weight Training

Dispelling the weight training myths:

"Weight training will ruin your golf swing," has often been the point of view of many golf "experts." In truth, however, weight training and the accompanying development of strength and power will help any golfer's game.

Many of today's professional golfers incorporate moderate amounts of weight training into their fitness routines. They know that muscular strength enables them to hit the ball far and straight. Far, because a strong golfer can generate more power than a weak golfer. Straight, because a strong golfer can manipulate the club with more precision than a weak golfer. Power and precision; an awesome combination!

Taking it to the limit:

Super Power Golfers do not just incorporate weight training into their routines - they milk it for all it's worth! Developing total body muscular strength, from head to toe, is one of the best ways to improve your performance in any athletic skill. A good strength base provides the foundation upon which a good golf swing can be built. Any golf professional will tell you it is much easier to teach sound swing mechanics to a strong person than it is to teach them to a muscularly weak person. Make up your mind that you are going to make weight training an integral part of your sporting life, especially your golfing life. It will be a decision for which you will thank yourself many times over the years.

Highly developed muscles - a hindrance?

There is no doubt that a regular weight training routine, especially the type of routine you will be learning in this book, will lead to stronger muscles. Stronger muscles usually become larger muscles. Does that mean you will "bulk up" to the point where you "get in your own way" as you try to swing the golf club? Not likely. Most people do not possess the kind of genetic potential to build huge muscles, no matter how much weight training they do. It would be a rare human being who could build so much muscular size that it would inhibit the golf swing.

Stronger muscles lead to greater speed in athletic movements. The golf swing movement is no exception. Highly developed muscles are an asset, not a hindrance.

Weight training for golf vs. "bodybuilding":

The type of weight training that will make you a stronger golfer will differ in many ways from the type of weight training that "bodybuilders" traditionally use. Bodybuilders are interested solely in the development of cosmetic muscle. They often perform four, five, or six workouts per week; some even work out twice per day. Each workout can often last 90 minutes or more. Rest assured that this is not the most effective type of workout schedule for a golfer.

Bodybuilders often divide their workouts into segments that specialize on one or two bodyparts, such as chest, back, shoulders, etc. Traditional bodybuilding instruction dictates that each muscle group be worked from a variety of "angles" with a number of different exercises. Bodybuilders also try to "isolate" the muscle(s) they are working; in other words they choose exercises and methods of exercise performance which tend to work only small areas of the body during any given movement.

Super Power Golfers need not worry about such matters; they work the entire body as one unit, striving to activate as many muscles and muscle groups simultaneously as possible. This is a much more efficient way to work out. Your weight training regimen as a Super Power Golfer will follow a logic that is superior to standard bodybuilding instruction.

General weight training guidelines:

1. Work the entire body as a unit.

Do not attempt to segment your training schedule into a "bodypart by bodypart" regimen. The human body is a system, not a collection of bodyparts that act and react independently of one another. You will make the greatest progress by training from "head to toe" in each and every weight training workout. Your workouts, while of brief duration, will be amazingly productive. You will have plenty of time for your body to fully recover between workouts.

2. Choose the most effective movements.

There are a handful of weight training movements that enable you to simultaneously use many muscle groups together; these are your best exercise choices. It is not necessary to try to isolate a muscle or muscle group when training with weights; in fact, that approach to training is highly inefficient. The movements you will be performing will allow you to let many muscles work together, which is one of the keys to developing power.

3. Train no more than two times per week.

Two weight training sessions per week, upon first impression, might not seem like enough workout time to accomplish any major gains in strength. As you gain experience, however, you will realize that the most productive workouts are those which are performed when you are physically fresh and fully rested. Twice per week will prove to be quite productive. You will also become aware, once you read chapter 4 of this book, that your typical week of physical training will also include 1-2 aerobic/conditioning workouts and 2-3 plyometric ball workouts. You will be getting plenty of exercise, believe me!

Your weight training workouts should take place on non-consecutive days. Eventually, as you get stronger, you will be capable of generating greater and greater levels of intensity in your workouts. The harder you train, the more recovery time you will require between workouts. Your workout frequency may eventually decrease to only three times every two weeks (once every four to five days), and then to only once per week. You will be fully refreshed and recovered for each and every workout.

4. Workouts should last a maximum of one hour.

That is, one hour from the time your walk into the gym until the time you leave. The actual weight training portion of your routine might be as short as 20 minutes. When you add in a warm-up period, some stretching, and a cool-down, the total time might be approximately 60 minutes maximum. Workouts that last more than 60 minutes are not being performed at peak efficiency.

By following the above guidelines, you will pave yourself a road to increased muscular strength and power. Through smart application, you will then be able to harness that power and convert it to longer, straighter shots on the golf course.

Terms you need to know:

Repetition - One complete movement of the weight in an exercise. Example: If you press a barbell one time over your head, you have done one "repetition," or, one "rep."

Set - A fixed number of repetitions done in succession. Example: If you press a barbell over your head ten times in succession, you have done one "set" of ten repetitions.

Momentary Muscular Failure - The point in a set where your muscles are too fatigued to lift the weight with proper form for even one more rep. When performing the programs in this book, only the final set of each exercise will be pushed to the point of, or close to the point of, momentary muscular failure.

Range of Motion - The complete movement capability of a joint. The weight training exercises in this book are not always done through a "full range of motion." For example, Super Power Golfers perform the deadlift exercise with the barbell starting from knee-level, not from floor-level. The leg press and bench press movements, likewise, are not done through the traditional full range of motion. The traditional concept of a full range of motion is often not applicable to the development of functional power. Super Power Golfers train for strength and power in that part of the range of motion where they have good leverage and can fully exploit the power of their muscles without risking injury.

Progression - The act of increasing, on a regular basis, the poundage's in one's weight training routine. Progression is the key to successful weight training; the main reason for training with weights is to become stronger as the weeks and months go by.

The best weight training exercises:

There are hundreds of weight training exercises to choose from. A select few, however, are superior in that they deliver the greatest strength gains in the shortest amount of time. Super Power Golfers do not waste time performing an endless variety of weight training exercises. They focus exclusively on the handful of basic movements that will maximize their results. Choose the best exercises, eliminate the rest of the exercises.

In this chapter you will find illustrations and explanations of four weight training movements and three abdominal movements. They represent seven of the best exercises for building basic strength and power. Is it really possible to develop super power through a regimen of only seven exercises? Yes, it is not only possible, it is inevitable if you hold true to your course; train hard, train brief, train only when physically and mentally at the "top of your game." The results will astound you.

The key movements:

Regarding weight training in general, there are three basic moves that your body might perform. They are: 1) upper body pushing, 2) upper body pulling, and 3) leg and hip thrusting. Your routine will include one movement for each of these functions, plus one overall power movement and three abdominal movements. This gives you your total of seven exercises. If it is hard to believe that you can get strong and powerful using only seven different exercises, well, you are in for a pleasant surprise. These movements are extremely effective in building head-to-toe muscular power.

The seven exercises:

1. The Deadlift (overall power)
2. The Leg Press (leg and hip thrusting)
3. The Bench Press (upper body pushing)
4. The Pulldown (upper body pulling)
5. The Abdominal Crunch (strengthens the midsection)
6. The Reverse Crunch (strengthens the midsection)
7. The Side Bend (strengthens the midsection)

Carefully study the descriptions and photographs of the seven movements. If you are unfamiliar with basic weight training, do not try the movements until you are fully comfortable that you understand what you are doing. The responsibility is on you to make sure that you are capable of working out safely and with proper form.

Weight Training Exercise #1: The Deadlift.

This is the "King" of all weightlifting exercises. Combining a powerful leg and hip drive with an upper body pull and back extension, it works every muscle group along the back side of your body. Special emphasis is on the lower back and buttocks. There is no other exercise that will strengthen the "erector" muscles of the lower back, or improve the total body power of a Super Power Golfer to the extent that Deadlifts will.

In the standard version of the Deadlift, the barbell is resting on the floor at the beginning of the movement. Super Power Golfers, however, begin the movement by having the barbell resting on a pair of boxes or a weightlifting rack that places the barbell at knee level. The bar should actually be touching your legs just above the kneecap as you begin the lift. Bend your knees. Grasp the barbell with an overhand grip. Keep your back straight and your head up (see photo 1-1). Keep the abdominal muscles tight. Stand up with the barbell. At the top position, you are standing fully erect, with the bar resting against your upper thighs (see photo 1-2).

Bending mostly from the hips, slide the bar back down your thighs to a point just above your kneecaps. Your back is always straight, never rounded. Your head is always up. Repeat for the desired number of repetitions.

Michael's super power tip: The bar should actually be touching your thighs at all times during the lift. As long as the bar is close to your body, chances of injury are minimized. Performing the Deadlift from knee-height maximizes your leverage and allows you to use heavier poundages. When performed in controlled fashion, with proper form, this movement can have a profound positive effect on lower back strength.

I cannot emphasize enough what a great overall power-building movement this is. If a golfer were to be given one, and only one, movement to master, this would be the best choice. Take a careful look at the photographs. The basic movement is simply "standing up" with the barbell. It is a very natural, functional movement. The deadlift, as pictured here, should form the basis of your golf weight-training workouts for the rest of your life.

Dr. King's comments: This is a great exercise for building strength in the lower back, thus avoiding injury to the vulnerable lumbar spine. By developing the surrounding musculature, the stress imposed on the low back in the golf swing is lessened. Also, the latest research has shown that the extensor muscles of the lower back have been markedly overlooked in the context of spinal rehabilitation. In addition, this is a wonderful exercise for building muscular endurance in the center portion of the body. This type of endurance enables a golfer to maintain a powerful, accurate swing through eighteen holes of golf.

Have you ever noticed that many golfers seem to "run out of steam" along about the fourteenth hole? What happens quite often, especially if you are walking the golf course, as opposed to riding in a cart, is that the lower back gets tired. When that occurs, the golf swing mechanics disintegrate because the low back/abdominal region is the "center" of the swing. Another point to consider is that chipping and putting require a strong, stable low back that will hold up throughout lengthy practice sessions or a full eighteen holes of golf. The Deadlift from-knee-level, when proper form is mastered, can serve as a real power booster for your golf game.

Weight Training Exercise #1: The Deadlift

Photo 1-1. Start position of the Deadlift; headup, back slightly arched.

Photo 1-2. Finish of the Deadlift; the barbell is always touching the thighs.

Photo 1-3. The Deadlift may also be performed with dumbbells. The technique is exactly the same as with a bar.

Photo 1-4. Note that at the top position there is no excessive backward lean. You should simply stand up into your normal posture.

Weight Training Exercise #2: The Leg Press.

This exercise develops the legs, hips, and buttocks. These are the strongest muscles in the body. The importance of strong legs and hips cannot be overstated. The beauty of this exercise is that a lot of weight can be used for many repetitions, which translates to a high power output.

To perform this movement, sit in a leg press machine. Most gyms will have at least one high-quality leg press machine. There are many different models, but any good leg press machine allows the user to sit in or lie upon a padded seat, with the feet pressed firmly against a solid platform. Place your feet squarely on the foot platform so that the entire surface of each foot is flush with the platform. Extend your legs until they are almost straight. Slowly bend your knees. Lower the weight until your legs are bent at a 90-degree angle (see photo 1-5). Going lower than this is not generally advisable, as it might place too much stress on the lower back for some trainees.

Extend your legs until they are almost fully straight (see photo 1-6). Repeat for the desired number of repetitions. Remember, lowering the weight to where the legs form a 90-degree angle maximizes leverage and promotes low-back safety.

Note: If you work out at home, and/or do not have access to a leg press machine, you may substitute an exercise known as "Wall Slides." To perform this movement, assume a standing position with your back against a wall. Slowly slide down into a semi-sitting position, then push back up to a standing position. Your back is always in contact with the wall. Repeat for the desired number of repetitions.

Michael's super power tip: Use a controlled, piston-like movement with a constant, driving cadence. Do not try to artificially slow down the thrusting movement of your legs as you push the weight up. Once you have learned this movement and have practiced the form with lighter weights, you should concentrate on developing maximum leg thrusting power. This is done by trying to move the weight fairly quickly; it should be heavy enough, however, to prevent you from moving it as fast as you are trying to move it.

The aforementioned advice is predicated on the fact that you should have full understanding of the proper form of the leg press movement, and that you are confident in your abilities to fully control the weight at all times. Again, the onus of responsibility is on you to learn the proper form before you try the exercise with weights that feel heavy.

Dr. King's comments: When we envision a powerful, athletic maneuver, we often think of the lower body and legs exploding with speed and grace. That combination is made possible through leg and buttock strength and flexibility.

The Leg Press delivers both of these benefits, and aids your upper body as well. Powerful legs provide the foundation for your swing and your follow-through. By staying strong, you can use the muscles of your legs and hindquarters to generate power without the undue torque that weaker golfers resort to in the attempt to generate club speed.

Weight Training Exercise #2: The Leg Press

Photo 1-5. Bottom position of the Leg Press.

Photo 1-6. Leg Press top position.

Photo 1-7. A type of leg press machine.

Photo 1-8. Another type of leg press machine. Regardless of the type of machine, the exercise technique remains exactly the same.

Weight Training Exercise #3: The Bench Press.

This exercise powerizes the upper body, especially the chest, shoulders, and arms. This is a basic upper body pushing movement. In most pressing movements the muscles of the chest, shoulder, and triceps (backs of the upper arms) work together to generate upper body thrusting power. The Bench Press is the pushing movement with which most individuals can move the greatest amount of weight.

Lie on your back on a bench pressing machine. Grasp the handles with a slightly-wider-than-shoulder-width grip. Press them to full arm's length (see photo 1-9). Lower to a position where your upper arms are parallel to the floor (see photo 1-10). Press back up to full arm's length. Repeat for the desired number of repetitions.

Michael's super power tip: Shorten the range of motion even more. There is often a "sticking point" in the bench press movement where the lifter's leverage is poor and the weight becomes very difficult to press upward. This point occurs on the bottom half of the movement. As the lifter attempts to drive the weight upward, poor leverage causes the lifter to get "stuck" and the lift often cannot be completed.

By restricting the range of motion to the "top half" of the lift, the Super Power Golfer gains better leverage and stays above the "sticking point." To gain even BETTER leverage and MORE power, further restrict your range of motion by lowering the weight a distance of only 4-6 inches. Bodybuilding purists may scoff at this technique, but the "top-range" bench press is a very functional way to build upper body thrusting power. Try it and you will discover that training in your "range of best leverage" is a great way to increase your power!

Dr. King's comments: Many golfers do not understand the need for upper body strength in a golf swing. The chest and arms create a link from your club to the rest of your body.

Proper bench press form is critical for this musculature to develop without injury. Pay close attention to Michael's instructions regarding hand placement. Your hands should grip the bar at points slightly wider than shoulder-width. I am not an advocate of "wide-grip" bench pressing, wherein the hands are positioned significantly wider-than-shoulder-width on the bar. This is an extreme position; this type of stress can lead to a season filled with the frustration and misery of rehabilitating a rotator cuff injury.

I can also appreciate the "short range of motion" suggestion (I give patients a similar technique when they have an already-injured shoulder) this allows them to perform the exercise without interference from the injury. The shoulder is not stressed at its weakest point; thus they get the muscular development benefits, minus the threat of further injury.

Weight Training Exercise #3 The Bench Press

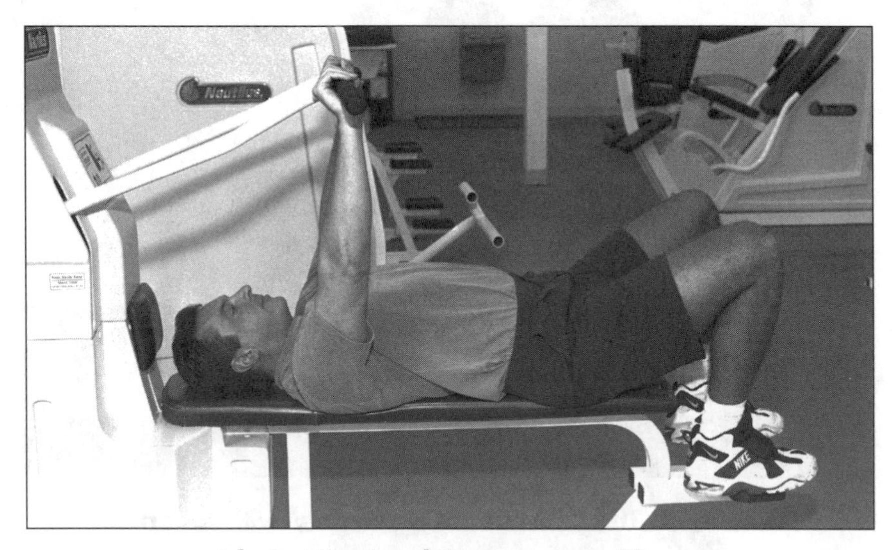

Photo 1-9. Bench Press top position.

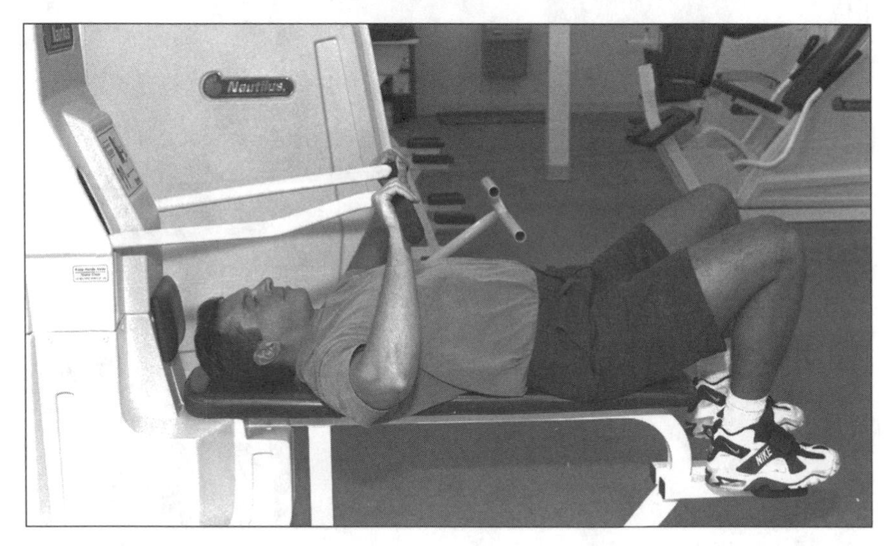

Photo 1-10. Bench Press bottom position. Upper arms are parallel to the floor.

Photo 1-11. The Bench Press performed with a barbell.

Photo 1-12. The Bench Press may also be performed with dumbbells.

Weight Training Exercise #4: The Pulldown.

This movement builds the back and arm muscles. It is a functional upper body pulling movement. The Pulldown has added value because it tends to give a good stretch to the arms, back, and shoulders.

Sit on a pulldown machine. If the machine has thigh pads, anchor your legs firmly beneath them. Use a handle that allows you to take an overhand, slightly wider-than-shoulder-width grip (see photo 1-13). Pull the bar down until it is at neck level, under your chin (see photo 1-14). Lean slightly back as you pull. Then let the bar return to the starting position with arms almost fully extended. Repeat for the desired number of repetitions.

Michael's super power tip: Pull with your arms and back as a unit. Conventional weight training advice often says something like this: "When performing lat Pulldowns, pull only with the back muscles; your arms and hands should serve only as 'hooks' that attach you to the bar; leave your arms out of the pulling action so that the back muscles can be made to bear the brunt of the work." This is poor advice. Your arms are made for pulling; there is no reason to leave them out of the action. When performing the Pulldown, relax your hands, then pull as hard as you want with your arms - that's what they're there for.

Dr. King's comments: The pulling-down-from-above motion decompresses the spine. It also stretches the muscles alongside the spine, giving them increased flexibility. This is a very important exercise for those golfers who have pre-existing low-back problems.

Low back problems are quite often caused by a lack of adequate space between the vertebrae of the lumbar spine. Riding in automobiles and golf carts for extended periods of time often worsens these conditions. The Pulldown is helpful in creating a stretching effect that can allow the lumbar vertebrae a little more "breathing room," which in turn can lessen the pressure on the vulnerable discs that act as cushions between the vertebrae. The end result of all this is a more fluid, powerful, unrestricted golf swing.

Weight Training Exercise #4: The Pulldown

Photo 1-13. Note the full stretch at the top position of the pulldown.

Photo 1-14. There is a slight backward lean at the bottom position.

Abdominal training; special notes:

During a golf swing, power begins in the lower body. To reach the upper body, power must pass through the midsection. A strong midsection is the Super Power golfer's greatest asset.

In terms of training the midsection, there are several long-standing misconceptions that must be clarified. First, there is the myth that there exist "upper" abdominals and "lower" abdominals This is not true. The entire front abdominal wall, known as the "rectus abdominus," is one muscle. This muscle's function is to draw the sternum (breastbone) and the pelvis (hip bone) toward one another. That is a very simple "crunching" movement. All abdominal exercises are essentially variations of this movement, thus there is no need to perform a high number of different abdominal movements. Nor is there a need to perform a high number of sets per exercise or a high number of repetitions per set. Indeed, your entire abdominal training routine should take no more than five minutes.

Treat your abdominals just like the rest of your body's muscles; train them by using the principles of maximum overload (use a weight or resistance that limits you to no more than 20 repetitions per set), and progressive resistance (an increase in the amount of resistance used over a period of weeks and months).

Three abdominal movements:

Three exercises will prove to be superior for strengthening your abdominal muscles. They are 1) the Abdominal Crunch, 2) the Reverse Crunch, and, 3) the Side Bend.

The Abdominal Crunch and the Reverse Crunch work mainly the aforementioned rectus abdominus (main abdominal wall). The Side Bend strengthens the obliques, which are the sheet-like muscles that run diagonally on either side of the rectus abdominus. The Side Bend also strengthens the very important quadratus lumborum muscles which stabilize the lower spine. These muscles are among the most easily-injured muscles in the lower back area; there can be no underestimating the importance of strengthening them.

Abdominal Exercise #1: The Abdominal Crunch.

The Abdominal Crunch fulfills the basic function of the abdominal wall; move the sternum and rib cage toward the pelvis (hip structure). This is a simple "crunching" movement; there is nothing fancy about it. Lie on your back with your feet over a bench. This keeps your lower body stable while your upper body moves up and down (see photo 2-1). Support your head in your hand and raise your shoulders up in the direction of your knees. Come up only approximately 4-6 inches (see photo 2-2). Lower back to the starting position. Repeat in a smooth, controlled manner for the desired number of repetitions.

Michael's performance tip: Initiate each repetition of the crunch by pressing the small of your back into the floor. When you lie on the floor, the normal curvature of your lower spine will create a space between the small of your back and the floor. By pressing the small of your back down into the floor, your shoulders automatically come up. This is the perfect crunching movement.

It is also interesting to note that the act of pressing the small of the back downward has another benefit; this action tends to "center" the pelvis and "flatten" the back. A properly placed pelvis and a relatively flat back help keep the abdominal wall from excessively protruding to the front. In other words, the crunch movement, properly performed, helps to flatten the abdominal wall not only by strengthening the muscles but by properly positioning and aligning the pelvis and lower spine.

When you are strong enough to easily perform two sets of 20 crunches, you should begin to add resistance by holding a weight plate against your chest with both hands. Start with a five-pound plate and work up gradually.

Abdominal Exercise #1 The Abdominal Crunch

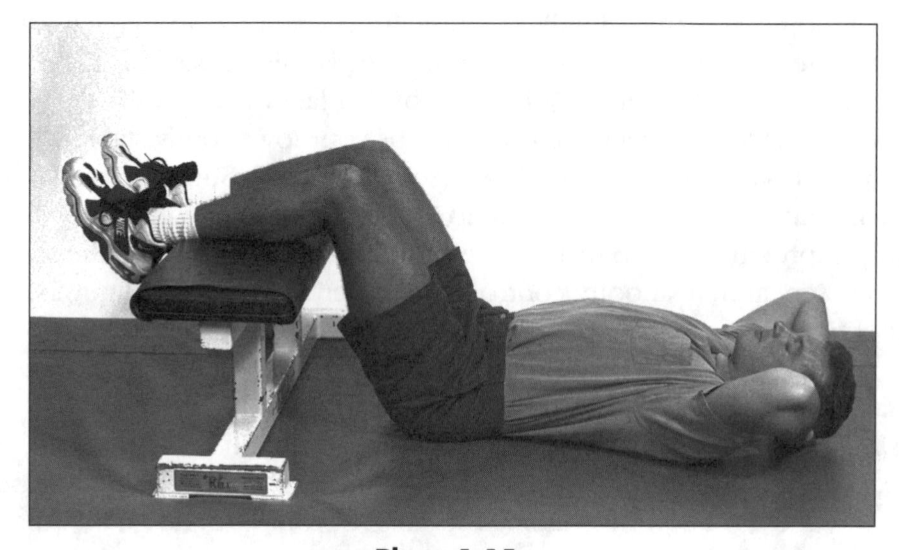

Photo 1-15.

Photo 1-16. The lower back is pressed downward into the mat during the abdominal crunch movement.

Abdominal Exercise #2: The Reverse Crunch.

This movement is similar to the aforementioned basic Crunch, except for the fact that your upper body is stable, while your lower body moves up and down. Lie on your back on an exercise bench. Use your hands to grasp the bench on either side of your head (see photo 2-3). Roll your hips up so that your knees move up toward your chin (see photo 2-4). This is a short movement; approximately six inches. Lower slowly back to the starting position. Repeat for the desired number of repetitions.

Michael's performance tip: Make sure you roll your hips upward, rather than simply drawing your knees toward your chest. The angle of bend in the knees remains constant throughout.

Abdominal Exercise #2 The Reverse Crunch

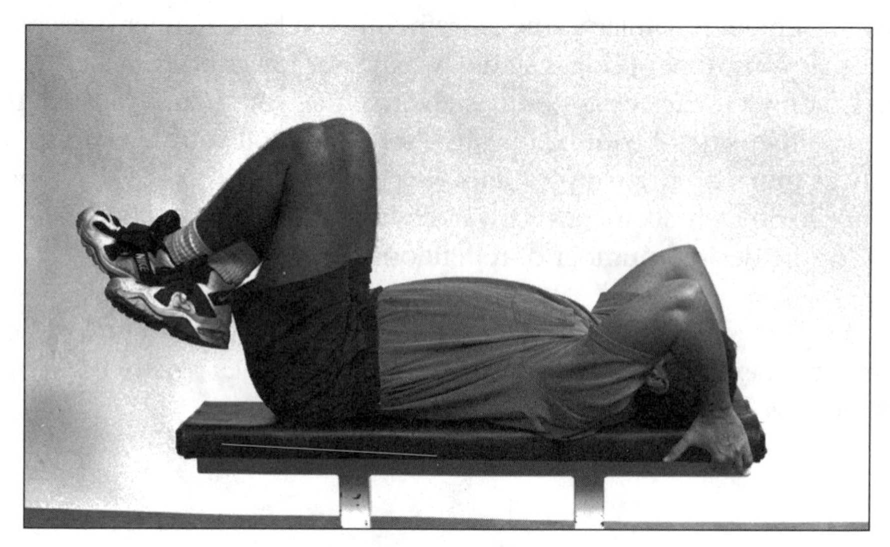

Photo 1-17.

Photo 1-18. The Reverse Crunch is a short motion; approximately 4-6 inches.

Abdominal Exercise #3: The Side Bend.

This movement, when performed correctly, strengthens the muscles involved in bending the body side-to-side. This movement requires careful attention to technique. Stand erect and hold a light (start with 5 lbs.) weight in one hand (see photo 2-5). Bend slightly toward the side of the hand holding the dumbbell (see photo 2-6). Return to the starting position. Perform the desired number of repetitions to that side, then switch the weight to the other hand and perform the same number of repetitions to that side. This is a slow, controlled movement that does not require a heavy weight to be effective.

Dr. King's comments: Abdominals are "guy wires" for the spine, giving it support, stability, and endurance. They allow the lumbar (lower) spine to move through a full range of motion without stressing the discs and other structures related to the spine. The abdominals, in other words, stabilize the spine when it is exposed to the stress of the golf swing.

"Extensor" muscles, or those of the low back, are also important. They allow the spine to endure the standing, walking, and addressing of the ball throughout a four-to-five hour round of golf. These muscles also contribute to power by engaging in the downswing. Extensor muscles are greatly strengthened by the Deadlift exercise explained in Chapter One.

Michael's comment: Several years ago I received a great tip involving the use of my abdominal muscles during the putting stroke. Here's what you do: just before stroking the putt, exhale in a short, quiet "grunting" breath and cramp down on your abdominals. By this I mean to flex your abdominals tight, as if someone were about to punch you in the stomach and you were tensing them to protect yourself.

Maintaining this tension in your abdominals, stroke the putt. It is amazing how this subtle action keeps your body still during the putting stroke. Try it and see if you don't sink more putts this way.

Abdominal Exercise #3: The Side Bend

Photo 1-19.

Photo 1-20.

2: Training Routines And Schedules

The anatomy of a workout:

Let us take a look at how a single workout might be structured. The entire workout, as mentioned earlier, should last no more than 60 minutes, from the time you walk in the gym until the time you leave. This mandates efficient use of your time. Considering all the major components of an effective workout, your hour-long session should be divided up something like this:

Warm-up:	Walking on treadmill or riding stationary bike - 10 minutes
Stretching:	Light stretching of any chronic problem areas - 5 minutes
Abdominal Training:	Two sets of each of the three movements - 5 minutes
Weight Training:	Maximum of four sets per exercise - 30 minutes
Stretching:	Relaxed full-body stretching - 10 minutes

That is a total of 60 minutes, which is ideal.

Setting up a training schedule:

The four weight training exercises and three abdominal movements are the focal point of your physical training for golf. All other factors, such as stretching and aerobic exercise, are considered to be secondary in importance to weight training. That is not to say that stretching, aerobics, and other factors are unimportant; very clearly they are part of the total package. Weight training, however, is priority number one. Full-body muscular strength is the Super Power Golfer's main goal. Weight training exercises are the nucleus of your program.

In review, the seven main training movements, with their basic functions in parenthesis, are:

1. The Deadlift (overall power)
2. The Leg Press (lower body thrusting)
3. The Bench Press (upper body pushing)
4. The Lat Pulldown (upper body pulling)
5. The Abdominal Crunch (strengthens the midsection)
6. The Reverse Crunch (strengthens the midsection)
7. The Side Bend (strengthens the midsection)

Sets and Reps:

In review: a repetition, or "rep," is one complete movement of the weight in an exercise. For example, if you press a barbell one time over your head, you have done one rep. If you press it over your head 10 times in succession, you have performed one set of 10 reps.

There is no magic formula for sets and reps in a workout. Some experienced weightlifters perform a high number of sets and/or reps, while others do not. In general, it is a sound strategy to perform between three and five sets per exercise, and to perform between 6 and 20 reps per set. That may sound like a large amount of leeway is being granted in structuring a workout; the fact is, however, that individuals vary greatly in their response and tolerance to exercise. Some trainees thrive on sets of 6-8 repetitions while others respond better to sets of 12-15 repetitions. Experience will be the force that guides the manner in which your workouts unfold.

The sample programs presented in this book will have you performing four sets of each weight training exercise, with repetition schemes falling between 6 and 20 reps. Follow the programs exactly when you are first starting out (especially if you are inexperienced at weight training). As you gain experience, you may want to make slight adjustments in the number of sets and reps you perform.

Guidelines to follow:

1. Perform no fewer than three and no more than five sets per exercise.

Only the final set of any given exercise should be performed at maximum exertion. Maximum exertion occurs when you terminate a set at the point of momentary muscular failure, which occurs when you are trying your utmost to perform one more rep, but you cannot do so because your muscles are momentarily fatigued. All sets preceding the final set should serve as progressively heavier warm-up sets. For example, if you are performing four sets of the Deadlift, and you know your goal for the final set will be to lift 100 pounds for 10 reps, your progression might go like this:

1st set: 50 (pounds) x 10 (reps)
2nd set: 70 x 10
3rd set: 90 x 10
4th set: 100 x 10

The first three sets should be well within your existing capabilities. The final set should be an all-out effort wherein you strive to better your past performance by using a little more weight for a comparable amount of reps. For example, if you succeed in lifting the 100 pounds for 10 reps in the above workout, your next workout's final set would entail a goal of 105 pounds for 10 reps; a progression of 5 pounds within the framework of performing 10 reps.

2. Perform no fewer than 6 and no more than 20 repetitions per set.

Again, there is no real magic in these numbers, but it does give you a framework. The important factor is that you consistently strive to become stronger within whatever set and rep scheme you choose.

3. Spend a maximum of 30 minutes on weight training.

This is a very important point. The authors have learned from experience that 90% of the benefits of a workout usually occur during the first 30 minutes of time; your energy reserves and powers of concentration begin to dwindle thereafter. Rest assured that 30 minutes of performing basic movements with challenging poundages is quite sufficient to promote steady gains in muscular strength.

Michael's favorite workout: I like to conserve my energy during the progressive warm-up sets, then "go for broke" on my final set of each exercise. To do this, I limit my reps to 6 per set during the warm-ups, then try for at least 10 reps on my final set. Using the deadlift exercise as an example, the progression might go something like this:

1st set:	100 (pounds) x 6 (reps)
2nd set:	115 x 6
3rd set:	130 x 6
4th set:	145 x 6
5th set:	130 x 10 reps or more

I find that this method of conserving energy helps me make faster and greater gains in strength than any other method I have tried. This set and rep scheme has been incorporated into the Golf Season workout program presented later in this chapter. Note again that all sets except for the final one should be well within your existing capabilities. The final set should be an all-out effort.

You are aware from your earlier reading that the maximum number of workouts per week you may perform is two. You are also aware that, as your strength and power increase, you will require a greater and greater amount of time between workouts; eventually you might only be training three times every two weeks, and then eventually only once per week.

A year-round schedule:

The year will be divided into three segments: "Off-Season," "Pre-Season," and "Golf Season." During each phase of the year, your priorities will shift; physical training will be of greatest importance during the "Off-Season" and "Pre-Season," while golf itself will be the priority during the "Golf Season."

Off-Season Program:

A four month period during which your primary goal is to build as much lean muscle mass and muscular strength as possible. For most golfers, the off-season occurs during the winter when golf is being played infrequently or not at all, and most of your time and attention can readily be given to a productive physical training program. Off-Season guidelines are as follows:

A. Training Frequency: Two workouts per week, spaced several days apart. Examples: Mondays and Thursdays, or, Tuesdays and Fridays, etc.

B. Workout Structure: The four weight training movements are split so that you perform two of them in your first workout of the week, and two of them in your second workout of the week. The abdominal exercises are performed in both workouts. Example:

Workout "A"	**Workout "B"**
Deadlift	Leg Press
Bench Press	Pulldown
Abdominal Crunch	Abdominal Crunch
Reverse Crunch	Reverse Crunch
Side Bend	Side Bend

C. Sets and Repetitions: 1) Weight Training Exercises - During the off-season, use the pyramid technique to increase your strength and power. Perform four sets of each weight training movement, increasing the weight on each set and decreasing the repetitions. Example:

Bench Press	1st set:	100 (pounds) x 20 (reps)
	2nd set:	115 x 15
	3rd set:	130 x 10
	4th set:	145 x 6

The first three sets are progressive "warm-up" sets; the final set should be an all-out effort requiring 100% of your strength to complete all the repetitions. 2) Abdominal Exercises - perform 2 sets of 12 repetitions of each of the three abdominal movements.

D. Progression: Each week, strive to add a small amount of weight to the second, third, and fourth sets. The first set can remain the same in terms of the amount of weight used because it functions solely as a light warm-up for your muscles and joints. Thus, a three-week progression on the Bench Press might look something like this:

	Week 1	**Week 2**	**Week 3**
1st set:	100 x 20	100 x 20	100 x 20
2nd set:	125 x 15	130 x 15	135 x 15
3rd set:	150 x 10	155 x 10	160 x 10
4th set:	175 x 6	180 x 6	185 x 6

You will notice that on the second, third, and fourth sets, the weight was increased by five pounds per week. The first set, as mentioned earlier, remains the same throughout the three-week period.

You may use the following chart to monitor your progress in the gym. For each exercise, record your sets and reps in the appropriate boxes.

OFF-SEASON PROGRAM
WORKOUT "A"
Date and Location:
Deadlift
Set 1 (20 reps)
Set 2 (15 reps)
Set 3 (10 reps)
Set 4 (6 reps)
Bench Press
Set 1 (20 reps)
Set 2 (15 reps)
Set 3 (10 reps)
Set 4 (6 reps)
Abdominal Crunch (2 sets of 12)
Reverse Crunch (2 sets of 12)
Side Bend (2 sets of 12)
Aerobic Activity:

OFF-SEASON PROGRAM
WORKOUT "B"
Date and Location:
Leg Press
Set 1 (20 reps)
Set 2 (15 reps)
Set 3 (10 reps)
Set 4 (6 reps)
Pull Down
Set 1 (20 reps)
Set 2 (15 reps)
Set 3 (10 reps)
Set 4 (6 reps)
Abdominal Crunch (2 sets of 12)
Reverse Crunch (2 sets of 12)
Side Bend (2 sets of 12)
Aerobic Activity:

Pre-Season Program:

A two-month period during which you are still training hard and heavy, but you are also setting aside time to practice golf (and perhaps to play golf if the weather permits you that luxury). Pre-season guidelines are as follows:

A. Training Frequency: Three workouts every two weeks, spaced four to five days apart. Example: Week One - Monday and Friday;
Week Two - Wednesday.

B. Workout Structure: The exercises are split into two separate workouts in a fashion identical to the Off-Season program. The two workouts are then alternated at the frequency of three workouts every two weeks. Example:

Week One:	Monday -	Workout "A"
	Friday -	Workout "B"
Week Two:	Wed. -	Workout "A"
Week Three:	Monday -	Workout "B"
	Friday -	Workout "A"
Week Four:	Wed. -	Workout "B"

C. Sets and Repetitions: 1) Weight Training Exercises - Switch your workout to a "four sets of eight repetitions" format. The first set is a light warm-up set; the second set is slightly heavier; sets three and four are then performed with a near-maximum weight.

Example:

Bench Press	1st set:	100 (pounds) x 8 (reps)
	2nd set:	115 x 8
	3rd set:	130 x 8
	4th set:	145 x 8

2) Abdominal Exercises - Perform two sets of 15 repetitions of each of the three abdominal movements.

Progression: Each week, strive to add a small amount of weight to the second, third, and fourth sets. The first set is always considered to be a warm-up set; thus, the weight does not have to be increased on that set.
You may use the following chart to monitor your progress in the gym. For each exercise, record your sets and reps in the appropriate boxes.

PRE-SEASON PROGRAM
WORKOUT "A"
Date and Location:
Dead Lift
Set 1 (8 reps)
Set 2 (8 reps)
Set 3 (8 reps)
Set 4 (8 reps)
Bench Press
Set 1 (8 reps)
Set 2 (8 reps)
Set 3 (8 reps)
Set 4 (8 reps)
Abdominal Crunch (2 sets of 15)
Reverse Crunch (2 sets of 15)
Side Bend (2 sets of 15)
Aerobic Activity:

PRE-SEASON PROGRAM
WORKOUT "B"
Date and Location:
Leg Press
Set 1 (8 reps)
Set 2 (8 reps)
Set 3 (8 reps)
Set 4 (8 reps)
Pull Down
Set 1 (8 reps)
Set 2 (8 reps)
Set 3 (8 reps)
Set 4 (8 reps)
Abdominal Crunch (2 sets of 15)
Reverse Crunch (2 sets of 15)
Side Bend (2 sets of 15)
Aerobic Activity:

Golf-Season Program:

The six-month period during which you play (and practice) the majority of your golf. Although golf may be your number one priority during this time, your workouts should still yield consistent gains in muscular strength. Training guidelines are as follows:

A. Training Frequency: One workout per week. Most of time will be spent honing your golf game, but you will be amazed at how productive your once-per-week workouts will be! With six full days of rest between each training session, you should be raring to go each time you step into the gym.

B. Workout Structure: You will now perform all four of the weight training movements, as well as the three abdominal movements, in the same session. Thus, your workout will look like this:

Deadlift
Bench Press
Leg Press
Pulldown
Abdominal Crunch
Reverse Crunch
Side Bend

C. Sets and Repetitions: 1) Weight Training Exercises - Now is the time to incorporate "Michael's Favorite Workout." Perform four sets of each weight training movement. The first three will be progressively heavier warm-up sets of 6 reps apiece. The last set should be an all out effort of 10-20 reps.

Example:

Leg Press	1st set:	200 (pounds) x 6 (reps)
	2nd set:	225 x 6
	3rd set:	250 x 6
	4th set:	225 x maximum reps

Notice that the third set is the heaviest set; the final set features a slightly reduced weight and as many repetitions as you can possibly do! 2) Abdominal Exercises - Perform two sets of 20 repetitions of each of the three abdominal movements.

D. Progression: Each week, try to slightly increase the total amount of poundage you can move on the final set of each movement. Calculate your poundage for the set by multiplying the number of reps times the amount of weight. For example, if you bench press 200 pounds for 10 reps, your total poundage for that set is 2,000 pounds (200 x 10).

This type of system gives you many options in your workouts. Use whatever combination of weight and repetitions which will increase your total poundage. Here is how one trainee might increase his bench press total poundage over four-weeks.

Week One: 200 (pounds) x 15 (reps) = 3,000 (total pounds)

Week Two: 215 x 14 = 3,010

Week Three: 185 x 20 = 3,700

Week Four: 200 x 19 = 3,800

You may use the following chart to monitor your progress.

GOLF-SEASON PROGRAM

Date and Location:

Deadlift

Set 1 (6 reps)	Set 3 (6 reps)
Set 2 (6 reps)	Set 4 (maximum reps)

Bench Press

Set 1 (6 reps)	Set 3 (6 reps)
Set 2 (6 reps)	Set 4 (maximum reps)

Leg Press

Set 1 (6 reps)	Set 3 (6 reps)
Set 2 (6 reps)	Set 4 (maximum reps)

Pulldown

Set 1 (6 reps)	Set 3 (6 reps)
Set 2 (6 reps)	Set 4 (maximum reps)

Abdominal Crunch (2 sets of 20)

Reverse Crunch (2 sets of 20)

Side Bend (2 sets of 20)

Aerobic Activity:

Special Considerations:

How heavy is "heavy"?

Quite obviously, "heavy" is a relative term; a weight that is heavy for one person may feel light to another person. If you are beginning a weight training program for the first time, plan on taking one to two months to train with weights that do not challenge your full physical potential. Common sense dictates that safety always comes first in an exercise program. There exists absolutely no reason to attempt to lift weights which feel so heavy that you are unsure of whether you can lift them safely; you should always know in advance that you are capable of performing each and every repetition with proper form.

Experienced weight trainees develop a sense of how "close to the edge" they can safely push themselves. Novice trainees lack this luxury, as their experience is too limited to allow them to make effective judgments in such matters. Again, if you are a beginner in the world of weight training, give yourself time to get used to the movements and to get a feel for how much weight you can safely use. No one is more responsible for your safety than you are.

Training at home vs. training in a gym:

A gym provides several advantages for golfers beginning a weight training program. First, gyms have a built-in safety factor: there are usually other people there working out who can aid you if you need help. Second, gyms normally have instructors available who can check your exercise form, give you tips, and answer questions you might have regarding physical training. Third, working out in a gym is a great way to meet other golfers.

Should you decide, however, that you would rather work out at home, rest assured that you can get just as good a workout in your own home as you can at a commercial gym. Rule number one, however, is "safety first," so make sure you have someone there who can help you if the unexpected should happen.

The "strength response":

Performing basic weight training movements which use many muscles at the same time triggers a "strength response" throughout the entire body. It is not accurate to say that there are "golf muscles" and "non-golf muscles." Many muscles work together in a golf swing. It is not important to know exactly what muscles are working during each exercise. It is important to know that by gradually increasing the amount of weight you can move in the basic exercises, your overall strength levels will greatly increase. Your entire body will get stronger. Your newly-built muscular strength will later be converted to power. Your drives will sail farther than ever before, and the precision of your iron shots will improve.

3: STRETCHING, FLEXIBILITY, AND WARMING UP

What is flexibility?

Flexibility is defined as the degree to which an individual is able to move his or her joints through their full range of motion. Some people are naturally more flexible than others. One's ability to develop extreme flexibility is, to a large extent, genetically predetermined. Other factors also affect flexibility. Young people are generally more flexible than elderly people, and females are often more flexible than males. Even such factors as the time of day (you are bound to be more flexible in the afternoon than in the morning) and your history of past injuries can affect flexibility levels.

What does stretching accomplish?

Stretching enhances the range of motion through which you can move your joints. Ideally, an athlete will have the ability to display muscular strength throughout the normal range of motion of each joint. This means that excessive flexibility, in the absence of accompanying muscular strength, is neither necessary nor desirable. The great majority of people already have an adequate level of flexibility relative to their needs. It is not important for you, as a golfer, to be able to touch your elbows behind your back or pull your foot up and around behind your head. The goal should be a level of flexibility that is adequate in terms of allowing a smooth, full golf swing.

If you can make a full, relaxed golf swing without undue tension building up at any point in the swing, then you can be fairly certain your flexibility level is adequate for a Super Power Golfer. Your personal stretching program can then be simply a maintenance program; as mentioned earlier, there is no need to attempt to develop excessive flexibility. Simply perform the stretches in this chapter at the end of each weight training workout, which means you will stretch a couple of times per week.

If, on the other hand, you cannot make a free-flowing swing, including a full backswing and a full follow-through, then you will benefit greatly from a consistent, persistent program to increase your flexibility. You will need to perform your stretching routine every day. Remember, do not stretch cold muscles - that means on a non weight-training day you will need to perform some kind of light aerobic exercise or calisthenics for 10-20 minutes before you stretch.

When is the best time to stretch?

Do not stretch muscles that have not already been warmed up. That means one would always stretch as late as possible in the workout.

The proper sequence for activities in an effective workout would be: 1) aerobic warm-up until the body's core temperature has been slightly elevated, which is usually signaled by "breaking a light sweat," 2) weight training, 3) stretching. Trying to stretch "cold" muscles may actually predispose them to injury.

The following five stretches, when accompanied by an intelligent, progressive weight training program, will accomplish the goal of developing adequate Super Power Golfer flexibility:

Shoulder Stretch

Keep palm of hand against door frame, with elbow bent at 90 degrees. Turn body away from fixed hand until a stretch is felt (see photo 3-1). Hold for 10-20 seconds. Switch arms and repeat. Do each arm three times.

Photo 3-1. Shoulder Stretch

Neck Stretch

Grasp one arm above wrist and pull downward and across back of body. Simultaneously, gently tilt head away from the arm you are pulling (see photo 3-2). Hold for 10 seconds. Repeat three times on each side.

Photo 3-2. Neck Stretch.

Upper Back Stretch

Place fingertips behind head, elbows pointed out (see photo 3-3). Gently push elbows in a rearward direction; back is slightly arched (see photo 3-4). Hold 10-20 seconds. Repeat three times.

Photo 3-3. Upper Back Stretch; start.

Photo 3-4. Upper Back Stretch; finish.

Hip and Buttock Stretch

Lie on back and draw one knee up towards chest. Cross bent leg over body and let hang 2-3 inches from floor (see photo 3-5). Shoulders remain flat on floor. Hold 10 seconds. Switch legs and repeat. Do each leg three times.

Photo 3-5. Hip and Buttock Stretch.

Hamstring Stretch

Lie down on your back and use your hands to support the back of your thigh behind the knee (see photo 3-6). Start with knee bent, then attempt to straighten the leg until a comfortable stretch is felt in the back of the thigh (hamstring). Hold for 10 seconds. Switch legs and repeat. Do each leg three times. This stretch also helps those golfers with tight lower backs, since tight hamstrings often lead to restricted lower back mobility.

Photo 3-6. Hamstring Stretch.

Is there a single best stretch for golfers?

This may sound strange, but the action of actually swinging a club is the best stretch for golfers. To state the obvious, you will stretch all the right areas when you perform your specific sports motion.

This leads us to a crucial point: do not make the mistake of marching up to the first tee and cutting loose with your best driver swing without first having warmed up. We have all been guilty of this careless infraction, have we not? Teeing off without warming up is an open invitation to disaster. There is no better way to injure yourself as a golfer than to violate the "always, always, always warm up" rule.

How should one warm up for a round of golf?

The ideal scenario for a golfer's warm-up would be: 1) a light aerobic warm-up, 2) stretching any chronic "problem areas" such as the lower back or the shoulders, 3) several minutes of swinging a golf club, which might or might not include hitting practice balls.

A light aerobic warm-up means 8-12 minutes of exercise that gets your heart pumping and elevates your core body temperature. Then, when you feel ready, proceed to 3-5 minutes of stretching any chronic problem areas you may have. Do not make the mistake of stretching without first doing a light aerobic warm-up. It is quite easy to strain muscles and/or tendons when you try to stretch them "cold."

There is a great exercise that is perfect for warming up the entire body for a round of golf. The movement is called the "Cross-Crawl;" it involves the combination of a marching-type step and a powerful arm swing (see photos 3-7 and 3-8). The movement has the added benefits of enhancing muscular coordination and improving posture. Perform it for 3-5 minutes; you will see marked improvement in the alignment of your body over a period of time.

The Cross-Crawl

Photo 3-7. The right arm swings up as the left knee lifts. The motion always involves simultaneous movement of the opposite arm and leg.

Photo 3-8. Now the left arm swings up as the right leg lifts; perform this movement as a continuous "marching" motion.

Michael's comment: Golfers belonging to private golf clubs may be able to take advantage of a growing trend: many private clubs now provide their members with fitness and exercise rooms. This is a wonderful thing; a brief session on an exercise bike or treadmill is a great way to warm up for golf. I have not yet seen any public courses with exercise facilities, but I would not doubt that some do exist. Perhaps in the future these facilities will become standard fare at golf courses; what a great benefit that would be!

Finish your warm-up by either swinging a club for a few minutes, or hitting a limited number of practice balls. Ten to fifteen balls should be plenty.

Tom Stevenson remarks: I recommend the following routine for the golf-skills portion of your warm-up: 1) Start at the putting green. First, get a feel for distance and green speed by rolling a few 30-40 footers. don't worry about trying to make them, just get a sense of rolling them the proper distance. In fact, rather than putting these long putts at a hole, you might try rolling them toward the fringe of the green, trying to stop them right at the edge. 2) Chip a few balls with various clubs, concentrating on striking them solidly and consistently. 3) Putt a few 3-footers. Stop as soon as you sink three in a row. This will bolster your mental image of the ball going in the hole. 4) Proceed to the practice range and hit 10-15 balls. Hit two or three short iron shots, a couple of mid-irons and long-irons, then finish with the driver or whatever club you will be hitting off the first tee.

It doesn't make sense to follow the traditional golf routine of hitting balls on the range first, then practicing your putting before you go to the first tee. It is better to putt first, then warm up on the range, then go to the tee fresh from having hit a few balls with your teeing-off club. That way, you will be more mentally and physically geared towards hitting an effective first tee shot.

4: PLYOMETRICS, AEROBICS, AND CONDITIONING MOVEMENTS

Plyometric exercise

The word "plyometric" means "to increase" or "to augment." Plyometrics are movements and exercises which train your muscles to react and function explosively, thereby increasing and augmenting your power. Power (the combination of strength and speed) is what this book is all about. Plyometric exercise, using a medicine ball, or "plyo ball," is one of the best ways to increase the power of your golf swing. Throwing the ball with a forceful movement of your arms, hands and wrists will add a "snap!" to your swing that will likely add 5-10 yards to your golf shots.

Plyo balls usually weigh any where from one kilogram (2.2 pounds) to 5 kilograms (11 pounds). They can be obtained at sporting goods stores or through mail-order catalogs.* For the purposes of exercises in this book we suggest a 1 or 2-kilogram ball for women and a 3-4 kilogram ball for men. One note of caution: if you have never used a plyo ball you must be very careful to get used to its weight before you try to throw it explosively. Beginners would be well advised not to throw the ball explosively until their 3rd or 4th workout. Warm up by tossing the ball back and forth with a partner until you are convinced that you can throw it with some "oomph!" without injuring your wrists or fingers.

Perform your plyo ball workout either with a partner or by throwing the ball against a gym wall. A racquetball court wall works well, although the noise factor might bother anyone playing on an adjacent court. Plyo balls, because they are heavy, make a resounding "thwack!" when they hit the wall. Perform the following plyoball routine 2-3 times per week on a year-round basis. The entire routine should take no more than 10 minutes. In terms of developing power, a little bit of plyo ball training goes a long way.

Perform each type of throw for 10-15 repetitions, waiting approximately 10 seconds between throws. The plyometric effect of each throw is enhanced if you have a partner who can toss you the ball; try to catch it and throw it in one smooth, yet explosive, motion. This will take some practice - remember, the ball is heavy - so don't put maximum force into your throws until you are accustomed to the weight of the ball. If you don't have a partner, simply make each throw as explosively as you can. Throw it off a gym wall; when it bounces back to you, gather it in and throw again.

Overhead Toss

Hold the ball in both hands. Draw it back behind your head. Step forward and throw it forcefully with a strong follow-through (see photos 4-1 and 4-2). You can also perform this toss while lying on your back (see photos 4-3 and 4-4).

Photo 4-1. Draw it back behind your head.

Photo 4-2. Step forward and throw it forcefully with a strong follow-through.

Overhead Toss - lying on your back

Photo 4-3. While lying on your back, draw it back behind your head.

Photo 4-4. ...throw it forcefully with a strong follow-through.

Underhand Toss

Assume a squatting position with the ball held between your legs with both hands. Toss the ball forward with an underhand motion (see photos 4-5 and 4-6).

Photo 4-5. ...with the ball held between your legs with both hands.

Photo 4-6. Toss the ball forward with an underhand motion.

Chest Pass

Hold the ball against your chest. Step forward and throw it straight out with a strong follow-through (see photos 4-7 and 4-8). You can also perform this toss while lying on your back (see photos 4-9 and 4-10).

Photo 4-7. Hold the ball against your chest.

Photo 4-8. Step forward and throw it straight out...

Chest Pass - lying on your back

Photo 4-9. Hold the ball against your chest.

Photo 4-10. ...throw it straight out with a strong follow-through.

Sideward Toss

Hold the ball down beside one hip. Toss it forcefully to the opposite side with an overhand motion and a strong follow-through (see photos 4-11 and 4-12). Perform this toss in both directions.

Photo 4-11. Hold the ball down beside one hip.

Photo 4-12. Toss it forcefully to the opposite side...

Golf-Swing Toss

Hold the ball to one side as if you were beginning a golf backswing. Using a golf swing motion, toss the ball forcefully to the opposite side (see photos 4-13 and 4-14). Follow through. Perform this toss in both directions. This is very important - do not neglect your non-dominant side. It is essential to the balance of your body and your golf swing that you practice this toss in both directions! You may also choose to perform this movement without releasing the ball. Hold onto the ball and swing it back and forth in a golf swing motion. This is tremendous exercise for your body's rotational musculature.

Photo 4-13. Hold the ball to one side as if you were beginning a golf backswing.

Photo 4-14. Using a golf swing motion, toss the ball forcefully...

Michael's comment: The combination of plyo ball tossing and weight training can take your golf swing power to new levels. Many of my golfing trainees have been astonished at the difference in their power after only a few weeks of plyometric training. This is a guarantee: Perform your plyo ball tosses 2-3 times per week for 10 minutes per session and you will add at least 5-10 yards to your drives!

*Companies that sell plyo balls include:

M-F Athletic Co. Cranston, RI 1-800-556-7464	Sports Training, Inc. Escondido, CA (619) 480-0558
Sissel Co., Inc. Murrietta, CA 1-888-4-SISSEL	Health for Life Los Angeles, CA 1-800-874-5339

Aerobic exercise?

Aerobic exercise is exercise that strengthens your heart and lungs. Strengthening the heart and lungs is also known as developing cardiovascular endurance. The development of cardiovascular endurance has been shown to have a beneficial effect on one's overall health and fitness.

To be completely honest, the game of golf does not place great demands upon one's cardiovascular system, therefore it cannot be stated for certain that performing aerobic exercise will improve one's golf game. The advent of the golf cart, quite obviously, made it possible to ride around a golf course rather than walk around a golf course. Thus, it is possible for a person to play golf even if that person has absolutely pitiful, or non-existent, cardiovascular endurance.

It is probable, however, that the healthier a person is overall, the easier it will be to play golf well, and enjoy it to the fullest. Aerobic exercise, therefore, is highly recommended to all golfers, Super Power Golfers included.

Aerobic exercise is dependent upon an adequate supply of oxygen delivery from the bloodstream to the working muscles. To qualify as being truly aerobic, the exercise must be able to be done non-stop for an indefinite period of time. An activity such as sprinting, for example, is not aerobic because one can only sprint for a short period of time, say, 20-30 seconds, before having to stop because of extreme muscular fatigue. Slow jogging, on the other hand, is aerobic because it can be continued indefinitely; the intensity level is low enough that the activity will not be brought to a halt because of muscular burnout.

Common examples of aerobic activities, provided they are carried out at low-to-moderate intensities, are walking, jogging, biking, rowing, in-line skating, aerobic dance classes, deep-water running, rope-jumping, and stairclimbing.

Which kind of aerobic exercise would most benefit golfers?

An interesting point to note is that aerobic exercise tends to be quite specific in the benefits it produces; for example, regular sessions on a stationary bike will improve your performance on a stationary bike, but will not make you a better swimmer. Conversely, swimming will make you a better swimmer, but won't necessarily improve your endurance on a stationary bike. Many golfers have encountered this phenomenon: they spend the winter pedaling away on an exercise bike, then find out during their first few golf rounds in the Spring that they are still surprisingly fatigued after walking the golf course. This leads to one very important fact: the best conditioning exercise for walking a golf course is...walking a golf course.

Rating the exercises:

The following chart rates some of the common aerobic exercises for efficiency in conditioning a Super Power Golfer. The exercises are rated from "5" (the best) to "1" (not recommended):

Outdoor Walking/Hiking: 5

As previously mentioned, this is the best conditioning activity because it most resembles what you actually do on the golf course.

Walking on a Treadmill: 4

Try to vary your walking speed and elevations as much as possible. Most treadmills allow you to do this at the push of a button.

Deep-Water Running: 4

This is a very interesting means of exercise; it is done in the deep end of a swimming pool while wearing a flotation vest. The vest keeps you afloat in an upright position while you move through the water by mimicking a running motion. For those who have a facility available and the desire for an unbelievable workout, this is a great exercise. It is especially beneficial to golfers with chronic back or knee pain, or those rehabilitating an injury.

Aerobic Dance Classes: 4

As long as the class is of low-impact style, wherein the stress on the knees, shins and other vulnerable areas is minimized, aerobic classes make a good choice for golf-related exercise.

Stationary Bike: 4

A good choice as long as you are using a high-quality bike. Set the seat at a height where your legs are almost fully extended at the bottom of the down-stroke. Make sure the tension on the bike is set at a moderate level.

Jogging: 2

Jogging is not recommended for golfers because it often leads to tendonitis and other types of over-use injuries. Jogging is notorious for tightening the low back and hamstrings, which is a big problem for golfers. Especially not recommended for golfers who are overweight; walking is a much better choice.

Rope-Jumping: 2

Generally not recommended, as there is too much impact on the feet and knees unless one is well-coordinated and proficient at jumping.

Swimming: 1

Not one of the better choices for a golfer because it is very easy to over-use the shoulder joints; swimming can also be hard on the lower back for those who are not proficient enough to maintain sufficient speed and muscle tension while moving through the water.

Michael's comment: I am one of those old-fashioned fellows who believes with all his heart and soul that golf is a game to be played while walking, not while riding in a cart. There is so much to enjoy about a golf course when you traverse it on your own two feet; that is when the true magnificence of the game manifests itself. I will not lie to you, however; I do at times rent myself a nice, comfortable cart and wheel my way around the course. If at all possible, though, I prefer to walk.

One problem I had in past years was that the act of carrying a golf bag on my shoulder for eighteen holes was causing my neck and shoulder to feel "out of whack" at the end of a round. Eventually I was experiencing neck problems that were becoming somewhat serious.

The problem, as explained to me by Dr. King, was that I was carrying the bag on my right shoulder all the way around the course; he suggested that I switch shoulders every hole.
This helped somewhat, but I didn't find a total solution until 1993, when I purchased a lightweight golf bag with a double shoulder strap.

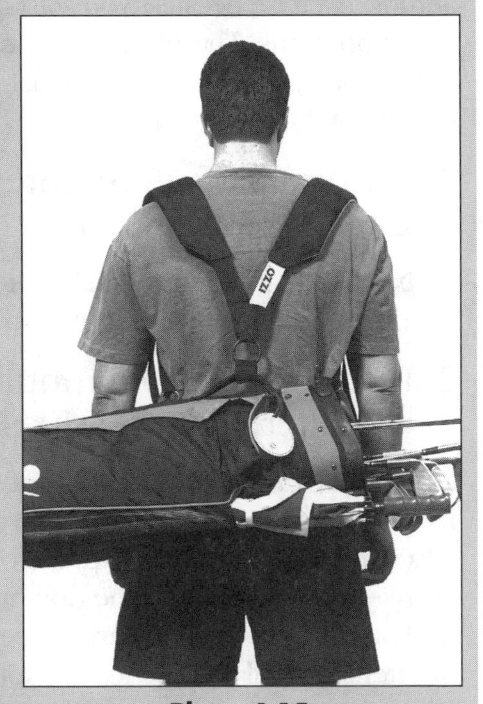

Photo 4-15.

If you have never seen this type of golf bag, do yourself a favor and find one in your local pro shop or golf store. The double strap enables a golfer to carry his bag in much the same manner as one would carry a knapsack; one strap goes over each shoulder and the bag is carried horizontally across the back (see photo 4-15). The weight of the bag, therefore, is quite evenly distributed across a large area and is much easier and more comfortable to carry than a regular bag.

This device gave new life to my neck and to my golf game. I was now able to carry my bag for 18, or even 36 holes with no discomfort either during or after a full day of golf. I strongly recommend this type of double-strap bag. Next to having one's own personal caddy, it is the best investment a golfer who loves to walk the course could make.

As previously mentioned, the act of walking a golf course will specifically make you more fit to walk a golf course. Such walking, however, is not true aerobic exercise because you start and stop too much; the exercise itself is not continuous. Therefore, if you really want to improve your true cardiovascular fitness, choose one or two of the aerobic activities previously listed and do one of the following:

1. Perform a 25-45 minute workout two to four times per week.

Exercise at an intensity that makes you feel mildly fatigued, but allows you to complete the 25-45 minutes without having to stop, or

2. Perform a 20-30 minute workout wherein you alternate intensities.

Alternate one-minute periods of easy exercise with 30-second periods of harder exercise. This is called interval training, and is recognized as one of the best ways to significantly improve one's cardiovascular fitness level. "Easy" exercise means just that; the one-minute "easy" periods should not physically tax you. The 30-second "harder" periods call for you to increase your speed or intensity until you are feeling somewhat out-of-breath, as if you would soon have to stop were you to continue at your present speed.

If you choose option # 2 above, you should realize that the descriptions "easy" and "harder" are terms relative to each individual. What feels "easy" to one person might feel "hard" to another person. You are an individual, training your individual body; there is absolutely no reason to exercise at a pace that makes you feel at risk in terms of your health. Do not push yourself harder than common sense and sanity would dictate. No one but you can feel what is going on in your own body while you are exercising. Do yourself the favor of exercising not only your body, but good judgment as well.

How should aerobics be integrated into a workout schedule?

Your aerobic workouts should be spaced throughout your week so that they do not interfere with your weight training workouts. Aerobic exercise is a supplement to the Super Power Golfer's all-important weight training routine. The optimal situation is that you will train with weights to develop total-body muscular strength, which will lead directly to becoming a better golfer, in addition to which you will enhance your cardiovascular fitness for reasons of all-around health and well-being. Here are examples of how to integrate aerobic exercise into your Off-Season, Pre-Season and Golf Season programs:

Off-Season Aerobics:

Since the Off-Season is the time when your priority is to build muscular strength through weight training, your aerobic sessions should be of low intensity. A good plan is to perform three 30-minute aerobic sessions per week; do them on days when you do not do any weight training. Example:

Monday - weight training
Tuesday - aerobics
Wednesday - off
Thursday - weight training
Friday - aerobics
Saturday - off
Sunday - aerobics

Again, these aerobic sessions should not be intense; they should feel rather easy and enjoyable. Your off-season priority is weight training; you should not expend undue energy on aerobic exercise and weight training at the same time. Simply do your three aerobic sessions per week to maintain a base level of cardiovascular fitness, and pour the main bulk of your energy into hefting those weights to get as strong as you possibly can.

Pre-Season Aerobics:

You have spent the Off-Season building up your strength; now you are about to decrease the frequency of your weight training workouts to three times every two weeks. this is the optimal time for aerobic interval training. Use the method of alternating one minute of "easy" aerobic activity with 30-seconds of "harder" activity; this will allow you to hone your overall physical conditioning for the upcoming Golf Season.

As weight training is still (as always) your number one exercise priority, you must once again space your aerobic workouts so that they do not interfere with your weight training workouts. To ensure that your energy levels remain high for each training session, schedule your aerobic interval training on a three-times-every-two-weeks basis; at this frequency you will make great gains in conditioning, while still allowing yourself maximum recovery. Here is a two-week example of how to set up your Pre-Season schedule:

Monday - weight training
Tuesday - off
Wednesday - aerobic interval training
Thursday - off
Friday - weight training
Saturday - off
Sunday - off
Monday - aerobic interval training
Tuesday - off
Wednesday - weight training
Thursday - off
Friday - aerobic interval training
Saturday - off
Sunday - off

Note that under this type of schedule you will never have to train two days in a row, which would be counter-productive to your overall energy levels. Note also that this type of regimen always leaves you with weekends free to practice or play golf.

Golf-Season Aerobics:

Golf season is a time to maximize your golf skills and golf enjoyment while still building muscular strength through once-per-week weight training. Aerobic training may now be relegated to the "back burner." If you consistently walk the course when you are playing golf, you may cut your aerobic workouts back to one 30-minute session per week (interval-style training is a good choice).

If you ride a cart when you play golf, you will need to perform two or three 30-minute sessions per week to keep up a decent level of aerobic conditioning. Basically, though, aerobic conditioning during Golf Season is your third priority, behind golf and weight training.

Above all, aerobic exercise should be enjoyable. Like weight training, it need not be done every day, rather, it should be done often enough to achieve optimal results, but not often enough that you grow weary of it. After all, only the great game of golf itself merits the lofty status of "let's do it every day!" Right?

Photo 4-16. Stationary biking is a wise aerobic exercise choice for golfers.

Photo 4-17. Vary your speeds and elevations while walking on the treadmill.

"Conditioning" movements for more PIZAZZ!:

There are three movements which are not purely aerobic, but which might prove invaluable in building up the muscular endurance of a Super Power Golfer. Described below, and illustrated on the following three pages, they are: 1) the Squat-Pull, 2) the Squat-press, and 3) the Bend and Press. Should you feel the need for more pizazz in your level of overall conditioning, try each of them for three sets of 30 repetitions at the end of your aerobic workouts. They will most assuredly provide an added jolt of intensity to your training session. Warning - they're not as easy as they look!

Conditioning Movement #1: The Squat-Pull.

Stand erect with an immovable cross-bar at collarbone level. Grasp it at slightly-wider-than-shoulder-width (see photo 4-18). Perform a deep knee bend to the point where your thighs are parallel to the floor (see photo 4-19). Simultaneously pushing with your legs and pulling with your arms, return to the starting position. Important: the bar is immovable, the only thing that moves is your body.

Photo 4-18. Start position of the Squat-Pull.

Photo 4-19. Squat-Pull bottom position.

Conditioning Movement #2: The Squat-Push.

Using an immovable cross-bar positioned just-above-knee-height, perform a push-up type movement using both your upper and lower body for power (see photos 4-20 and 4-21).

Photo 4-20. Start position of the Squat-Push. This is similar to a push-up.

Photo 4-21. Finish position.

Conditioning Movement #3: The Bend and Press.

Hold a pair of light dumbbells at shoulder height. Bend into a semi-squat position (see photo 4-22). Simultaneously push with your legs and press with your arms so that you stand fully erect with the dumbbells high overhead (see photo 4-23).

Photo 4-22. Bottom position of the Bend and Press.

Photo 4-23. Top position.

5: Common Golf Related Injuries

By Dr. Neil King

Adopt a "conquering" attitude:

I want you to view this section with real enthusiasm. I am not just talking about feeling better, I am talking about playing better. If you do have a bad back, or any other golf-related injury, it can be overcome. Weight training and stretching, combined with appropriate rehabilitative exercises and a healthy dose of determination, can keep you playing long after a golfer with a lack of knowledge and commitment has been forced to give up the game.

Golf is a contact sport:

You may not think of golf as a contact sport, but there is a high incidence of golf-related injuries. Many of these injuries occur at the point of impact, when the club strikes the ball and/or the ground. Remember, good players strike the ball first, then the ground (on their iron shots), and bad players often strike the ground when they are aiming at the ball (the dreaded "fat" shot), so golf can be considered a contact sport.

Many golf injuries are inflammation-type injuries (such as tendonitis or bursitis), or muscle strains, which are actual tears in muscle fiber. Quite often, these injuries are caused by inadequate warm-up of the muscles and joints. Another common cause is overuse, or "over-doing it," usually stemming from too much practice (i.e. hitting too many buckets of balls on the driving range) or playing too much golf after an extended layoff. The number one contributing factor to golf-related injuries, however, is faulty swing mechanics. In other words, a poor swing can hurt you in more ways than just raising your golf score.

Any golfer who thinks he/she may be injured should immediately consult a physician, preferably one who specializes in sports-related injuries. An injured area's rate of healing is often directly related to the speed with which the injury is diagnosed; the sooner treatment begins, the more quickly the injury will heal. It is never a good idea to try to "play through" an injury; the healing process will be disrupted and, in all likelihood, your swing will change in ways that are undesirable.

In this chapter, we will briefly discuss five common types of golf-related injuries: 1) lower back pain, 2) shoulder pain, 3) elbow pain, 4) neck/upper back pain, and 5) wrist pain. We must also reiterate the importance of warming up the muscles and joints before a round of golf, and the benefits of limiting one's practice time. That's right, no "300-practice-balls-per-day" routines!

Lower back pain:

Has your back ever felt stiff after a round of golf or a day at the driving range? If so, you are certainly not alone, and the problem is not limited to amateur golfers and "duffers." The number one reason players retire from the pro golf tour due to disability is low back pain! This brings up an important rule for Super Power golfers: if you want to play and enjoy this game for a lifetime, you must make physical conditioning a priority now. The weight training, stretching, and aerobic conditioning programs in this book should serve as your training "bibles" for years to come.

Structure of the low back:

The low back is made up of five large, moveable bones called vertebra. Between these bones are cushions composed of fibrocartilaginous material - think of them as sponges - which are called discs. Discs, when they are traumatized, can become misshapen (bulging), thus irritating nerves.

Discs are what get removed, either partially or completely, when a person has back surgery. This is usually done to relieve pressure from a branch of the sciatic nerve, which is the nerve that runs down into the leg and gives it strength and sensitivity. The discs must twist with every golf swing, and believe me when I say that discs do not like to twist.

What then can be done to keep the discs happy and in their proper positions (away from the nerve routes), so that we can continue to enjoy our beloved game of golf? Stretching and strengthening the musculature surrounding the lower back and abdomen helps keep discs "peaceful and quiet," and allows us to make smooth, powerful swings. By now you are surely getting the message that strong, supple musculature and good swing mechanics go hand in hand as the two most important factors in leading both to healthy backs and impressive golf shots.

The "long and short" of it:

Regarding the lower back, you should be aware that most injuries and fatigue in the spine occur when a player is using his longer clubs, such as the driver, fairway woods and long irons. The torque and stress involved in a golf swing is greater with the long clubs than with the short irons and wedges, so strive continually to improve your swing fundamentals and swing mechanics; this will lead to less stress and, of course, better shots. Also, the better you strike the ball, the farther your tee shots will go; therefore, the fewer fairway woods and long irons you will have to resort to on your approach shots. You'll be hitting short irons and wedges more often.

The "one-sided" blues:

The problem with golf and our spines is that golf is a one-sided sport with excessive and repetitive twisting involved. For a right-handed player, the left side of the body is asked to stretch, then abruptly shorten in order to bring the clubhead squarely back to the ball with high velocity. If you lack suppleness and strength in your low back and hips, you will not easily be able to generate the necessary clubhead speed involved in a solid strike of the ball.

Many golfers, in an effort to artificially generate more speed, resort to various lunging and "whipping" movements to compensate for their lack of power in the swing. A healthy spine will enable you to strike the ball with more force, and to generate that force with less conscious effort, thereby lessening the chance you will injure yourself in the process. You can see that a strong, healthy low back makes it easier to make a fundamentally sound swing.

Two tips for "balancing" your back:

Tip #1: Learn to swing in the opposite direction.

If you are a right-handed golfer, take your five-iron, hold it in your right hand, and swing it like a lefty; in other words, swing it in your "opposite" direction. Do it five times; this will stretch the right side of your back on the back swing, and will tighten the right side on the downswing. Learning to swing in the opposite direction is one of the most important skills a golfer can teach himself. Practice this!

Photo 5-1.

Photo 5-2.

This drill will not only balance your back, it will balance your swing as well. This occurs through a process called "kinesthetics," the human body's sensory mechanism for knowing where it is in space. This really works! Do this just before you strike your first balls of the day. Remember, swing in the opposite direction from your normal dominant side, and do it five times only. Your playing partners may cast you some questioning glances, but be secure in the knowledge that you are preparing your body for a smooth, yet explosive and powerful swing. This drill also greatly enhances one's ability to make a strong follow-through in the golf swing.

Tip #2: Determine whether or not your legs are equal in length.

A shorter leg and a tilted pelvis can cause major problems in your back and in your golf swing. This problem is not uncommon! You will serve yourself well to do the following test: Stand in front of a mirror, with the top of your pelvis (hips) exposed. Look closely. If one side is shorter than the other, you might have a short leg. It is impossible to have a healthy spine and a strong swing with one leg noticeably shorter than the other! This tip might have you laughing out loud, but I have treated countless golfers who had this syndrome.

A right-handed golfer will normally exhibit this problem in the right leg; such a golfer will almost always be plagued by a persistent slice of the golf ball. The problem can often be alleviated by using a small heel lift device worn in the shoe. If a wild slice has been bedeviling you on the golf course, check the length of your legs. Your slice might soon be a thing of the past!

Shoulder pain:

Not a golfer exists who has not at some point experienced some sort of problem with the shoulder joint in their lead arm (for a right-handed golfer this would be the left shoulder). Shoulder pain is so common among golfers that I have often been inclined to coin a new phrase: "golfer's shoulder."

The shoulder joint has a unique design which allows for tremendous mobility, but comparitively little stability. This means that the shoulder joint can be moved and rotated in many directions through a very full range of motion, but that it is also quite easily injured. The joint is rather loosely held in place by supporting ligaments, tendons and muscles.

Have you heard the term "rotator cuff?" Well, the infamous "cuff" is actually a group of muscles that have their origin in the back and shoulder blade, wrapping around to the front to give the upper arm bone support and function. The rotator cuff area is extremely vulnerable to injury; in fact, very few athletes in any sport escape rotator cuff problems for an entire career.

Most shoulder injuries occur from over-use, or from improper technique. The more times you swing a golf club, the more chance you have of overusing the joint to the point where inflammation might occur. It makes obvious sense to learn the proper golf swing technique; the better your swing, the more good shots you will hit. The more good shots you hit, the lower your score will be, and the less you will have to swing the club. Here again, a common theme emerges: the best way to avoid shoulder joint injuries, or injuries of any type, is to develop a better golf swing!

Exercises to help the shoulder:

By performing a few simple exercises, you can actually increase the range of motion within the shoulder capsule itself, thus achieving greater flexibility. The added flexibility will allow for greater clubhead speed by increasing the arc through which your clubhead travels. Here are two helpful exercises:

Exercise #1: Pendulum movements.

Hold a light weight (less than five pounds) or a five-iron in one hand. Bend forward so that your back is roughly parallel to the floor, bracing your free hand against a chair or bench for support. The arm holding the weight should hang straight down; with that arm, trace twenty-five small circles and twenty-five "figure 8's." Do this once per day, making sure to always do it one hour before playing golf or hitting balls. This maneuver will help "lubricate" the joint and provide for enhanced mobility.

Exercise #1: Pendulum Movements

Photo 5-3 Pendulum Movements.

Exercise #2: Broomstick exercise.

This is my favorite exercise for helping golfers safely improve their shoulder rotation. Assume the body positioning of your normal golf stance. Hold a broomstick (or a golf club) in front of you, parallel to the floor at waist-height, gripping it with both hands at shoulder width (see photo 5-4).

Slowly rotate your hips to the left (if you are a right-handed golfer), using your right hand pushing against the broomstick to move your left arm away from the midline of your body (see photo 5-5). Slowly return to the starting point. Repeat five times. Note that you turn only to the left, then return to the starting point. You do not turn to the right at all.

You must relax your upper torso completely to perform this movement properly; that is the only way to achieve full motion in the shoulder joint. If you fail to relax completely, you will get little or no benefit from this movement. You can actually increase the overall shoulder girdle range of motion with this exercise; your hip turn will increase as well. Proper practice of this move will help you achieve a full follow-through with a "high-hands" finish to your swing.

Perform this maneuver five times before your first tee shot, then an additional five times when you make the nine-hole turn. Remember, rotate in only one direction. Right-handed golfers rotate to the left; left-handed golfers rotate to the right. In other words, you are rotating in the direction of your normal swing.

Exercise #2: Broomstick exercise

Photo 5-4. Start position of the "broomstick" exercise (here shown using a golf club).

Photo 5-5. In the finish position, use the right hand to push the left arm and shoulder up and around.

Additional comments:

Shoulder injuries are common in all athletes over the age of 35, and extremely common in golfers over the age of 50. If you feel that your shoulder has in some way become injured, put ice on it immediately; this will help control any inflammation and swelling in the damaged tissue. Once swelling has occurred, it is difficult to return the joint to its full range of motion, so ice is a crucial first step in treatment of shoulder injuries. Apply the ice for a fifteen-minute period every two hours. If pain persists for more than 36 hours, consult a sports injury professional for advice. A qualified professional will steer you in the right direction before loss of mobility becomes long term and adhesions (scar tissue) from.

Elbow pain:

Again, the more golf you play, or practice, the more likely you are to develop this type of injury. Inflammation of the tendons near the elbow is quite common among golfers who play more than twice per week, and/or golfers who have flaws in their swing technique.

Golfers who do not properly "follow through" in their swings are especially prone to "golfer's elbow" (pain on the inside of the elbow) injuries. Gripping the club too tightly or striking the ground (or driving range mat) too hard are two other common causes of elbow trouble in golfers.

This is probably an appropriate juncture at which to interject a personal opinion: I hate those range mats! I am often amazed at the number of patients I see each year who have injured themselves due to repeatedly striking balls off of driving range mats. Many of these mats are mounted on an asphalt base. Hitting one or more buckets of balls from a threadbare range mat is a great way to really beat up your left arm, left elbow, and neck. The repetitive shock your body must absorb is equivalent to using a jackhammer! Adding insult to injury is the fact that quite often at the range you are "working on" your swing; thus, you are bound to mis-hit the ball, at least on occasion.

A slightly better choice is to find a range mat which is mounted on a plywood frame; at least then there will be some "give" when your clubhead strikes the mat. The best choice, of course, is to find some nice velvety grass to practice from. If you must hit from mats, take your time between shots, and make sure that your hands and wrists are relaxed when you swing.

Neck/upper back pain:

The neck and upper back play an integral role in a smooth, powerful golf swing. The neck and head provide a pivot and focal point for an effective follow through. Over the years I have seen countless golfers develop poor habits in their swing tempo because their neck problems make them tentative in striking the ball. In a good golf swing the head and neck remain relatively still. If your head and neck shift abruptly during the swing, of if they must dissipate the shock created by striking the hard ground with your club, you are heading for trouble.

Neck pain also often results from the fact that the golf swing is such a one-sided action, always moving in the same direction. As mentioned earlier, it is a great idea to develop your ability to swing in both directions, and to do so on a regular basis. Another factor which can cause neck problems is the common habit many golfers have of tilting their head to one side to trigger the swing. Jack Nicklaus probably popularized this move more than anyone; he makes a pronounced chin tilt away from the ball just before he swings the club. Surprisingly, though, this subtle movement can eventually cause a one-sided tension in the neck region.

A bad neck can "eat away" at your game and take the fun completely out of golf. It is interesting that a golfer with a bad back will sometimes say that the injury has helped his game because it makes him relax, concentrate, and release the hands and wrists more to decrease pressure on the spine. Golfers with bad necks never make such comments; rather, they often complain that they "ache all over" after a round of golf, and often express disgust that they made the effort to play at all! I have much sympathy for these golfers; I know how frustrating it can be to try to strike a golf ball crisply when your neck is giving you problems.

Maintaining a positive attitude and strengthening the neck:

There is hope for golfers with bad necks; the answer lies in strengthening the neck and upper back so that pressure is taken off the neck region, which is also called the "cervical spine." The cervical spine is a very compact structure made up of seven vertebra. The vertebra in the neck region allow for great mobility so that the head may swivel and tilt in a variety of directions. The discs between the cervical vertebra provide cushioning and spacing for nerves to exit from the spinal column and branch out into the arms and upper back. It is these discs, and thus the exiting nerves, that will benefit from strengthening the neck and upper back muscles.

Refer to chapter 1 of this book. The Deadlift and Pull down exercises in the weight training section can do wonders for strengthening the neck/upper back region of the body. There is also a great home exercise you can do for your neck; it requires no equipment other than a bed or a padded bench. Lie face down with your head hanging off the edge of the bed or bench. Lift your head slowly to a neutral position (parallel to the floor) without arching your neck. Hold for three seconds, then lower your head slowly. Repeat 15 times.

By strengthening the muscles which help to hold up your head, you are building support for your swing. An advanced variation of this exercise would have you holding your hands on top of your head, then gently raising your head slightly past the neutral position. Hold for a two-count; repeat 15 times. Do not attempt the advanced version until you can easily perform the basic version of this exercise.

Avoid the "herky-jerk":

Again, as always, proper swing technique also helps in preventing the development of injuries. "Herky-Jerky" swings inevitably cause abrupt weight shifts and arm motions which are quite unnatural. That is, as you can imagine, a big problem for your neck; the discs simply do not like abrupt motion; indeed, I have seen some golfers whose swings are so "fast, furious, and faulty" that I speculate an average round of golf for them is the equivalent of eight or ten "whiplash" injuries within a four-hour period! Ouch!

If you suffer a neck injury, apply ice to the injured area as soon as possible. Keep the ice on for 10-minute intervals, waiting one hour between applications of the ice pack. Should you experience any pain radiating down the arms or legs, see a doctor immediately; loss of strength can occur soon after numbness develops. Resume playing golf only after you have regained a full range of motion in your neck region, and are able to turn your head easily to look in both directions. Returning to the course or practice tee too soon will risk further damage that may cause you to miss a lot of golf time; it's not worth the risk!

Wrist pain:

Any sport which requires the forceful "firing" of the wrists during a swinging motion can lead to wrist pain and injury. Golf certainly fits the bill; indeed, the wrists are one of the most vulnerable areas on a golfer's body. Quite often, the wrists can be injured when the impact of the clubhead on the ground sends a "shock wave" up the club shaft into the wrists and hands. This often happens when a golfer hits a shot "fat."

This type of pain in golfers will most often occur in the area directly beneath the bony portion of the wrist bone on the pinky finger side of your wrist area. If this area presents you with chronic problems, ice it for 10 minutes after you play or practice.

"Warming up" before a round of golf:

The warm-up, as we have mentioned earlier in this book, is a critical element of a Super Power Golfer's game. Power golf requires optimum flexibility and quick "firing" of the muscles. It does not make sense to demand power and precision from the body without first preparing it for action; to do so is to "beg" for an injury!

Review chapter 3 of this book. Gentle stretching of the legs, hips, back, shoulders, elbows, and wrists is recommended before a round of golf. Ideally, a 15-20 minute ride on a stationary bike would precede the stretches. This might present a slight inconvenience, but believe me, it works!

"Hit 300 practice balls per day?" No way!

During a golf swing, small units in our bodies are constantly being asked to stretch and contract within a millisecond of time. By packing many repetitions of the golf swing into a short time span, a golfer subjects the muscles surrounding the joints to fatigue and possible spasm.

Hitting 300 balls per day is a sure-fire way to invite overuse-type injuries. Far better to hit 30 quality practice shots per day, concentrating on the pre-shot routine and target-selection. In regards to practice, more is not better, better is better.

Michael's comment: This may sound strange, but I truly believe the following statement: The less skilled you are at golf, the less you should practice your full swing.

Think about it for a moment. If you do not have the basic skills and sound fundamentals to make a series of proper golf swings, then what exactly is it that you are practicing? You are simply grooving your bad habits, and in the process you are probably beating the heck out of your back, shoulders, elbows, neck and wrists. First make sure you have learned the proper fundamentals of grip, stance and swing before you begin to rack up the hours on a practice range. A good teaching professional who gets you off on the right track fundamentally is worth his or her weight in gold, not only because your golf scores will be lower, but because the potential wear and tear on your body will be greatly reduced.

The time will come when you have grooved an effective, repeating swing which enables you to make a smooth swing motion time after time; only then will you be truly able to reap the benefits of extended practice time.

Finicky feet:

A friend and I were playing golf one day; he was walking down the first fairway in front of me after we had thrashed our drives off the first tee. I noticed that Mark's golf shoes were extremely collapsed at the heels; they were sagging markedly towards the insides of his feet. In biomechanics we call this hyperpronation. "How long have you been wearing those shoes?" I called to him. "You need to buy some new ones."

He turned to me with an incredulous look on his face. "Dr. King," he said, "I just bought these shoes in the pro shop before we teed off. I've only been wearing them for five minutes!"

I was stunned; he had walked less than 200 yards in his brand new shoes and they already looked like they were collapsing (I wish I owned the pro shop where he buys golf shoes - I could sell him a new pair every day!). I have since fit him with orthotics and discussed some foot exercises with him, but we are still searching for a brand of golf shoe sturdy enough to withstand his excessive heel motion. At one point he found a "high-top" brand of golf shoe that seemed to work quite well, but the manufacturer no longer makes that particular brand of shoe.

Mark's foot problems point out an interesting fact about golfers' feet; proper foot motion is a critical factor in a powerful swing. The feet serve as the foundation for the knees and hips to pivot and glide upon.

A foot problem like Mark's is not uncommon; it usually originates from overly tight calf (lower leg) muscles, and can actually cause a loss of power in the swing because the knees and hips "follow the lead" of the feet in generating power. Two simple exercises can help to decrease the tension in the calf muscles:

Calf stretch

Stand with the ball of your foot on the edge of a step. Lower your heel until you feel a gentle stretch in the arch of your foot and in the muscles of your calf (see photo 5-6). Hold this position for 15 seconds at a time. Repeat 10 times on each foot. Do this exercise at least once per day, and always before heading out to the first tee.

Photo 5-6. Calf Stretch.

Foot raise

Stand flat-footed. Raise the front of one foot off the ground, as if you were trying to touch your toes to your shin while keeping your heel on the ground (see photo 5-7). Perform three sets of 15 repetitions with each foot. This exercise strengthens the tibialis anterior muscles which run along the "shin" area.

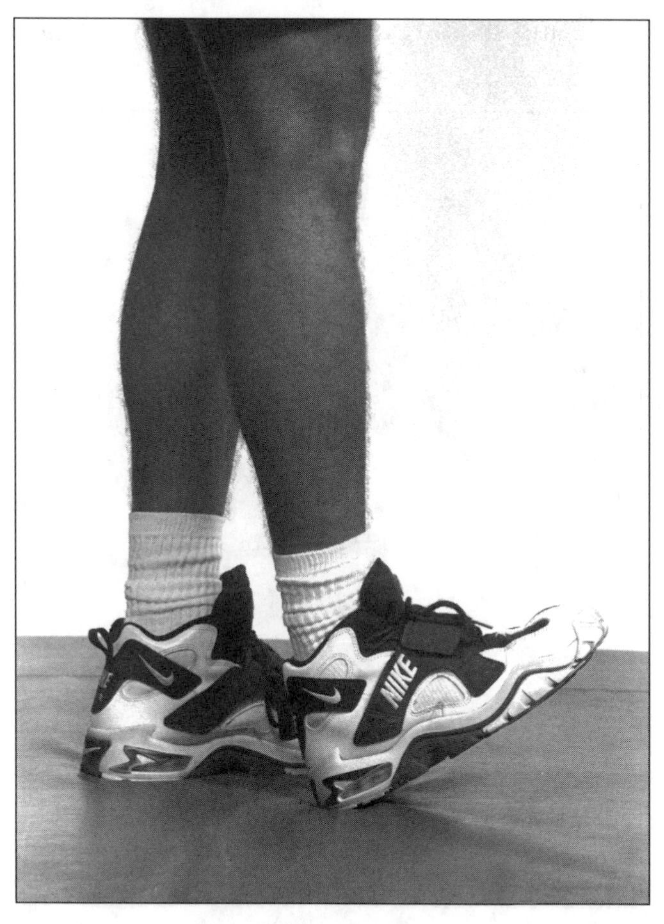

Photo 5-7. Foot Raise.

3 Exercises golfers should never do:

1. Mimicking the golf swing while holding a dumbbell in one hand.

This "exercise" (see photo 5-8) is one I commonly see golfers do in the gym. It is a very bad idea. Swinging a dumbbell in this fashion creates harmful torque and "movement of force" which can injure the low back and neck. The acceleration of the weight imposes great stress on the shoulder, too; this is not at all desirable and should be avoided. Practice your golf swing with a golf club, not a dumbbell.

Photo 5-8. Swinging a dumbbell.

2. Swinging two or three clubs at the same time.

I often see golfers do this (see photo 5-9) while waiting to tee off on the first tee. Not good. The excessive weight of the combined clubs and shafts creates a too-great momentum in the backswing and follow-through. This can injure the shoulder and/or elbow due to having to hold the clubs with an awkward grip. Additionally, the momentum can injure the low back and neck during the follow-through. Note: a "donut" weight on a single golf club does not present these inherent difficulties, and thus is a safer way to warm up.

Photo 5-9. Swing 2-3 clubs at once.

3. Rotating trunk with club held across shoulders.

This movement (see photo 5-10) is "insulting" to the discs in the lower spine. Bending forward while rotating in this fashion is particularly dangerous - don't do it!

Photo 5-10. Rotating with club.

Using a stretchcord to prevent injuries and develop power

A simple device called a "stretchcord" can help tone your golf muscles and improve your posture. This can lead to more power in your swing. A stretchcord is a length of rubber tubing with a handle attached to each end (see photo 5-11). Attach the middle of the cord to an upright immovable object. Grasp the handles and you're ready to go. Stretchcords are available in most sporting goods stores. The three exercises pictured here may be done four times per week. Perform each movement for one to two minutes each session. You will soon be able to feel your posture improving and your swing will have more *oomph!*

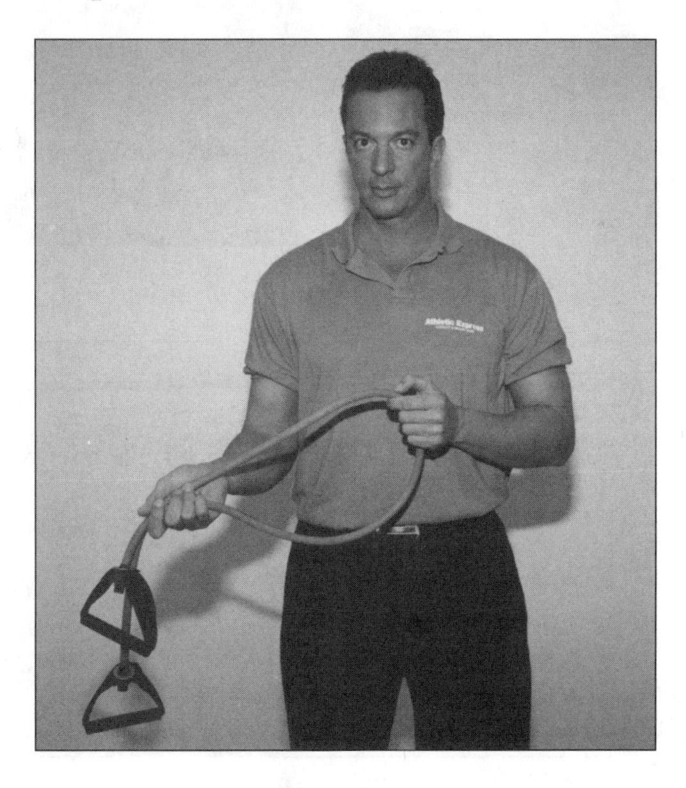

Photo 5-11.

The Pivot

Grasp the handles and pivot your body back and forth, pulling the handles alternately in to your waist (see photos 5-12 and 5-13). As one hand is pulled in to the waist, the other hand is extending away from your body. Do this continuously for one to two minutes.

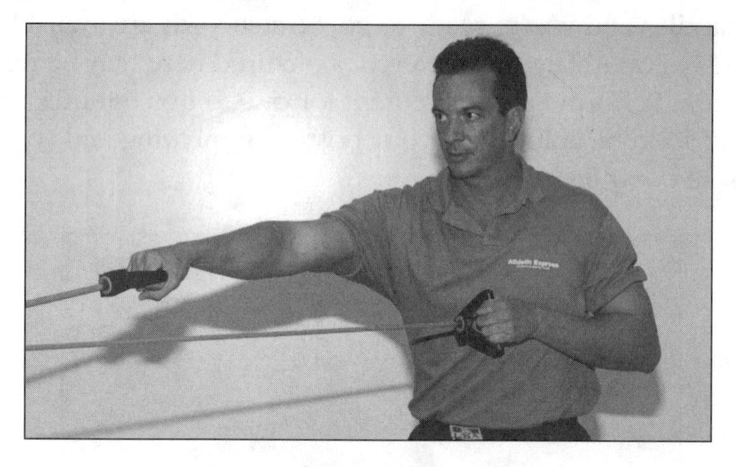

Photo 5-12.

Photo 5-13.

The Double-Arm Pull

Grasp the handles with both arms extended in front of you (see photo 5-14). Pull both handles simultaneously in to your waist (see photo 5-15). Return to the starting position. Do this continuously for one to two minutes.

Photo 5-14.

Photo 5-15.

The Single-Arm Stretch

Grasp one handle with your arm extended across the front of your body (see photo 5-16). Step sideways and pull the handle away from your body (see photo 5-17). The cord will stretch across the front of your body. Do this continuously for one to two minutes.

Photo 5-16.

Photo 5-17.

Quirky ways golfers get injured:

Many strange things happen on golf courses. I have known golfers to incur injuries in a variety of "oddball" (but common) ways. Here are some of them:

1. Strained lower back when lifting golf bag out of trunk. This one is very common. Lifting a golf bag out of your trunk should be done just like the Deadlift exercise in weight training. Bend your knees slightly, keep your head up, maintain abdominal tone, and keep the bag close to your body as you lift it out. A back strain could otherwise be lurking!

2. Strained shoulder caused by pulling a club from the bag and starting to walk away before the club is all the way out of the bag. Club gets caught, extended arm gets a nice little wrench and - ping! - strained shoulder! Happens all the time.

3. Twisted ankle from stepping in unseen hole. Golf courses are full of such devilish little traps - it really pays to keep your eyes open while traversing the hallowed grounds of your local links. Another common occurrence: twisted knees and ankles suffered when jumping across ditches or creeks on the course, especially with one's golf bag across one's shoulders. Not a good idea!

4. Bruised/bashed/twisted/mangled extremities resulting from driving one's golf cart with the left foot sticking sideways out into the air. Now here is a serious accident waiting to happen. A foot sticking out in this fashion can connect with just about anything (tree stumps, bushes, boulders, fence posts, or just humps and bumps in the ground) and the injuries can be very serious indeed. Please keep your feet inside the cart!

5. Bumps and bruises occurring when golf balls ricochet off branches, fences, etc. and reconnect with foreheads, eye sockets, collarbones, etc. Now, can you really play a low cut shot around that tree, or will it just turn out to be (painful) wishful thinking?

Persevere:

Remember, golf injuries, while not a rare occurrence, can be overcome. It takes a moderate amount of knowledge and a liberal amount of perseverance in performing simple exercises, but the results are well worth the time invested. We all want to play this game for a long time to come, and in most instances there is no reason why that desire cannot become a reality. Play on!

6: THE POWER GOLF SWING

An Interview with Thomas Stevenson, P.G.A. Professional

Is the swing an athletic move?

A powerful golf swing resembles the athletic move made in many other sports. Imagine a batter in baseball; his power comes from his weight shift and hip turn, along with a delayed release of his wrists. In fact, the golf swing and the baseball swing are nearly identical, except for the fact that they occur on different planes (the golf swing is obviously more upright than the baseball swing).

In many ways, a golf swing also resembles the throwing motion of a football quarterback, or even a boxer throwing a punch. The shifting of weight first slightly away from, then fully toward the target, creates the impetus for power.

How can a golfer make "all the right moves"?

It is important to remember that in the golf swing, as in other similar sports movements, the "right moves" occur automatically; they do not have to be consciously manipulated as the action takes place. Do you think that heavyweight boxing champion Joe Louis, as he threw a knockout punch, ever thought, "okay, cock the right arm slightly back; now shift the weight and really put the hips into this one..." Of course not. He had trained himself to start each punch from a position of power; the punch itself was simply a releasing of coiled, or stored energy.

Likewise, in golf, it does not make sense to try to think about all, or any, of the positions of the club, or the position of your body, during the swing. Most athletic power moves occur in the blink of an eye; the golf swing is no exception. A good golf instructor teaches his/her students to store energy on the backswing; the downswing is then simply an uncoiling, or releasing of stored energy through the ball.

Take note of the phrase "through the ball." This is an important point. In all powerful athletic moves, energy is released toward the target. Think again of the baseball batter, the football quarterback, or the Olympic discus thrower. There is a tremendous releasing of energy outward toward the target. Golf is no exception. While the golf swing is more leisurely than a batter's swing or a discus thrower's explosive toss, it is crucial to finish the swing. Golfers who swing to the ball, instead of through the ball, seldom have a powerful swing.

What mental images might help lead to a better swing?

There are two mental images which come to mind when picturing the golf swing action. The first is an image Sam Snead used with his students to demonstrate the proper acceleration of the clubhead in the swing. Imagine you are holding a pointed stick, approximately the length of a driver. Impaled on the pointy end of the stick is a big round apple. Imagine swinging that stick so that the apple is hurled over a fence. This imagery reminds the golfer not to release the power of his swing too soon, or he will simply slam the apple straight into the ground.

Another technique: imagine the golf club is a sledgehammer and the ball is a spike pointing toward the target. If you try to pound this spike into a heavy piece of wood, you will naturally shift your weight into the hit, while allowing the weight of the hammer to assist you in generating power.

Michael's comment: Images such as "throwing the apple over the fence" and "driving a spike with a sledgehammer" are very helpful to me. I am a big fan of this type of imagery as an aid in learning what a good golf swing looks like and feels like. It seems to me that using such imagery is a much easier way to learn the golf swing than is trying to break the swing down into all its separate positions and learning each one of them.

At some point, years ago, somebody somewhere decided to make a stop-action series of photos depicting the golf swing from address position to completion of follow-through. That person then analyzed each position of the swing and offered commentary as a means of learning the swing.

I believe that whoever the "pioneer" was who invented this method of instruction did us all a disservice, because what resulted is a virtual library of comments telling us that "the right hip does this" and "the left shoulder does that" and "the right elbow should be here" and "the left knee should be there."

How can anyone swing a golf club with all those thoughts in mind? I know I can't. It's much easier for me to "flow" with a certain visual image, preferably one that is very simple.

Another point to be made: don't discount the power of imitation. Children often learn many skills simply by imitating others. This is a great way to learn the golf swing. Standing in front of your television set and "swinging like the pro's do" is, in my opinion, one of the better ways to groove a smooth swing. Hopefully you won't take any divots out of the carpet, or bang a nice chunk out of the corner of a wall (both of which I have been guilty of). Tom Stevenson once pointed out to me that most golfers play much better if they play immediately after watching a tournament on T.V.

I am not a golf teaching professional, but I occasionally find myself presenting the basic fundamentals to beginning golfers. One woman had never swung a golf club in her life. I spent a minute showing her how to hold the club, then a couple more minutes making smooth, balanced swings and having her imitate me.

I then placed a single golf ball in front of her and said, "This is the only ball you get to hit today. Fire away!" Using a men's stiff-shafted 5-iron, she proceeded to make a beautiful swing and scorched a gorgeous 150-yard shot over a pond that was near the practice tee. The act of imitating had helped her learn to feel good swing tempo. The act of setting an example for her with my own swing had helped me reinforce my own concept of good swing tempo; thus, we both benefited from the lesson.

What constitutes a powerful position at address?

Here's how to assume a "position of power" when addressing the ball:

First, make sure that your balance in the address position is strong. Place your feet approximately shoulder width apart. Shorter golfers may stand with their feet slightly wider, while taller golfers are usually more balanced with their feet slightly narrower-than-shoulder-width.

Your back foot should be perpendicular to the target line, with your front foot turned out towards the target approximately 20 degrees. Make sure that your weight is on the insides of your feet. Make every possible effort to have all parts of your body (shoulders, hips, stance, etc.) lined up parallel to the target line.

You should have a feeling of relaxed power: poised, ready and confident that you are about to make a smooth, powerful swing that will launch the ball straight to the target. Remember, also, that you should be aiming at something very specific; it is amazing how many golfers hit shots without having made a clear mental picture of exactly what the target is. If you are aiming from the tee down the fairway, aim at a specific part of the fairway. If you are hitting to the green, try to knock the flag stick down! Never hit a ball, either on the course or on the practice range, without first having taken aim at a specific target.

Photos 6-1, 6-2, and 6-3. In terms of balance and dynamics, the full swing should resemble the plyometric ball "golf swing toss" you learned in chapter 4. When the center of gravity remains stable throughout the swing, explosive impact is the result. Your arms will whip the clubhead past your body and through the ball. Shots will fly straight and true to the target. The full-release finish position is a direct result of two things: 1) a sound position at address, and, 2) a stable center of gravity during the swing. If you swing to a full finish with perfect balance, you can almost be assured of a shot that is both long and accurate.

What is the single most important factor in developing a powerful swing?

The most important factor is clubhead speed at impact. Different golfers generate that speed in different ways. The swings of Jack Nicklaus, Arnold Palmer, and Chi Chi Rodriguez, for example, appear very different from each other. Nicklaus uses a strong hip turn and a fast leg drive. Palmer, who has often been described as having arms like a blacksmith, makes a fast arm swing past a very steady head position. Rodriguez seems to be very wristy.

For all golfers, strong leg, hip, lower back and midsection muscles will help create power no matter what type of swing is used. Also, strong hands and wrists are always a plus. At some point in a round of golf, unless you play with the accuracy of a Ben Hogan, you will encounter situations where you literally have to "muscle" a shot, such as when hitting from heavy rough or other types of bad lies. In general, a golfer with strong hands can better manipulate the clubhead through the impact zone.

Also, don't discount the chance that when you shake hands with your opponent on the first tee during the club championship, you might be able to intimidate him or her if you possess an extra-powerful grip. After all, every little trick helps.

How does a golfer's stance affect power?

It is important to use a stance that correctly places the body's center of gravity in accordance with the golfer's height. A shorter golfer, as previously mentioned, will usually benefit from a slightly-wider-than-shoulder-width stance, whereas a taller golfer normally is more balanced with a shoulder-width stance. In fact, a golfer's ability to keep a stable center of gravity is a key factor in a balanced, powerful swing, so the width of a golfer's stance is more important than one might think.

How does a golfer's grip affect power?

For most people, I advocate a slightly "strong" grip; that is, for a right-handed golfer, both hands should be rotated slightly clockwise, or to the right, of a "neutral" position. One way to check this is to make sure that, as you look down, you can see at least two, and possibly three, knuckles of your left hand when you are gripping the club. This hand position works well for most golfers because it places the left hand in a more powerful "karate chop" position, as opposed to a "slap with the back of the hand" position. The main point to look for in an effective grip is that the palms should pretty much be facing each other.

Very few great golfers have had highly unorthodox methods of gripping the club. Look at pictures of the all-time greats like Hogan and Arnold Palmer. You will see that their grips, while they may vary somewhat in terms of being slightly "strong" or slightly "weak," are usually rock-solid and give an appearance that a powerful blow can be delivered. Their hands appear to be molded to the golf club.

How does the average golfer lose power?

An improper, or non-existent, weight shift is the main reason amateur golfers lose power. Equate this to other sports: in throwing a ball or swinging a bat, it would never be effective to do so while falling backward. It is the same in golf; the weight must shift forward as the downswing begins. This brings us back to our discussion of the importance of keeping a stable center of gravity. The swing must have a center. A golfer's center of gravity is basically a point located on the midline of the body, approximately four inches below the navel. It is around this point that the swing revolves.

If your center of gravity remains constant throughout the swing, chances are good that you will hit a fine shot. If you "sway" backwards away from the ball on your backswing, as many golfers do, then you have obviously moved your center of gravity. You will then have to make some kind of compensatory move on the downswing, which in the case of most amateurs means a sort of sliding motion to try to get the clubface back squarely to the ball. Often this results in the clubface not meeting the ball squarely, and an errant shot results.

When your center of gravity remains stable during the swing, a proper weight shift occurs naturally; there will be a slight shifting of the weight to the inside of the back foot on the backswing, followed by a full shifting of the weight to the front foot on the downswing. These actions will, as I said, occur naturally if the golfer retains a stable center of gravity and refrains from excessive swaying and sliding during the swing.

If you watch professional golfers on television, you will notice that it is difficult to see any pronounced shifting of the weight on the backswing. There are two pivot points in the golf swing: the weight of the upper body is loaded into the right hip (for a right-handed golfer) at the top of the swing; it then flows smoothly into the left side during the downswing. An expert golfer will finish with nearly all his weight on the front leg and foot. The reason everything looks so smooth and effortless is that, once again, the center of gravity moves very little during the swing.

One point that cannot be stressed enough is that the weight remains on the inside of the rear foot during the backswing. Once the weight gets outside that back foot, it is very difficult to contact the ball squarely on the downswing. One could thus state that the most visually dramatic portion of the weight shift is the forward shift to the front foot during the downswing, and that this shift will occur smoothly if the center of gravity has remained stable during the backswing.

Dr. King's comments: I have worked with hundreds of golfers over the years, rehabilitating their injuries and striving to maximize their performance. A proper weight shift is, in my mind, the one factor most often missing in the swings of folks who injure their backs and/or shoulders playing the game. They fail to realize the importance of engaging the body's major muscle groups to achieve balance and flow in the swing motion.

When your body is balanced and your swing flows, you avoid the improper skeletal torque that often leads to injuries. The use of the legs to provide a solid, yet agile, foundation has the dual benefit of increasing the power of your shots and decreasing the likelihood of injury.

The use of the legs is an oft-misunderstood aspect of the golf swing. Here's a loose analogy: imagine trying to row a boat without using your legs. Not very effective, is it? Now imagine incorporating a free-flowing leg drive to your boat-rowing technique. Feel the power of your legs engaging and achieving nearly full extension before your arms really do any work at all. That is the same type of smooth flowing leg drive that can allow power to blossom in your golf swing. In rowing, we say that the legs do eighty to ninety percent of the work. Imagine approaching that same ratio in your golf swing.

The smooth transfer of weight from the inside of the back foot to the ball of the front foot provides the foundation for the swinging arms and shoulders to deliver the clubhead squarely to the ball. Imagining your swing as a canoe or kayak free-flowing down a river will give you a good sense of the kind of rhythm and tempo your golf swing should have.

When the center of gravity remains stable throughout the swing, explosive impact is the result. Your arms will whip the clubhead past your body and through the ball. Shots will fly straight and true to the target.

This full-release finish position is a direct result of two things: 1) a sound position at address, and, 2) a stable center of gravity during the swing. If you swing to a full finish with perfect balance, you can almost be assured that the resulting shot is zeroing in on the target like a miniature cruise missile.

What is the most important club in the bag?

For the average golfer's enjoyment of the game, the driver is the most important club in the bag. If you can put a solid drive out there in the fairway, with adequate distance, your outlook is going to be better about the whole game. Besides, who cares if you're a good putter if you're always putting for double bogey? Learn to drive the ball straight and far. Remember, as previously discussed, that you should always have a specific aiming point.

You can also experiment on the practice range with a number of visualization techniques to help you hit different types of drives. For example, if you want to hit a low, hard tee shot, imagine you are driving the ball under a bench placed several feet in front of you. That mental picture will help you "stay down through the shot" and finish with your arms extended low towards the target. Conversely, if you want to hit a high tee shot, imagine you are hitting over a tree or a building in the fairway; you'll then release fully to a high finish.

Michael's comment: "My lesson with Tom Stevenson" - Back when I first started playing golf I had absolutely no power to my iron shots. My short iron shots would always be high pop-ups "down the right field line." One day I was visiting Tom at Hell's Point Golf Club in Virginia Beach, I persuaded him to give me some help on the driving range. Strolling along in his relaxed manner, he followed me to the practice tee, calmly munching on a tuna sandwich (whole wheat bread, no mayo).

"Hit a few balls with your 8-iron," he said. I did so. Each ball arced weakly off the clubface, dying a pitiful death at a point barely beyond the 100-yard marker. I looked at him forlornly, shrugging my shoulders in resignation. "Stand farther from the ball," he said. I moved a few more inches away from the ball and swatted another shot. It soared majestically into the blue sky, magnificent in its graceful flight.

My spirits buoyed, I hit another shot, then a second and a third. Each ball followed the same wonderful high-arching path, hanging in the air for what seemed like an eternity before plopping to earth within spitting distance of the 150-yard sign.

Overjoyed, I turned to share my moment of triumph with Thomas. He was already 50 yards away, ambling back to his favorite swivel-stool in the pro shop, casually polishing off the last bite of his tuna sandwich.

What are some common characteristics of great golfers?

Most great golfers have exceptional overall body coordination, as well as excellent hand-eye coordination. They are superior in regards to possessing, mastering, and displaying the motor skills related to golf.

These great golfers, in addition, possess an intangible "something" that allows them to perform at peak ability on the golf course. Many golfers can go to the driving range and strike every single ball beautifully - it seems they can do no wrong. Then they get on the course and something happens; they can't hold up under the pressure, even if that pressure is self-imposed. Perhaps it is the fact that on the course, each shot is "final;" there are no second chances. "Mulligans," remember, are an invention no respectable competitor would ever take advantage of.

Great golfers have the will to win, the killer instinct; they perform as well, or better, in the clutch than when there is nothing on the line. It has often been said that Arnold Palmer could "will" the ball into the hole on an important putt. Jack Nicklaus himself has said that he thrived on the feeling of playing the last two holes of a major championship in even par while the other contenders "collapsed" around him.

In all sports and athletic contests, those who thrive on pressure usually achieve the greatest success. This brings up an important point. When you are on the course playing a casual round of golf, or even a match against your buddies, why would you impose so much pressure on yourself? It's not the U.S. Open out there - loosen up and go for it!

What is "smart aggression"?

A Super Power Golfer should employ a strategy of smart, aggressive golf, rather than timid, defensive golf. A Super Power Golfer knows his strengths, and attacks the course accordingly. He or she plays with confidence; always playing the percentages, yet striking the shots boldly and firmly. Seldom is it a good idea to "take something off the shot." Too often this results in a weak, pushed shot instead of one that flies true to the target.

"Zeroing in":

It is also important to have an exact target on every shot. I don't mean to over-do this point, but it is all-important. Do not strike that ball without first forming a definite, precise picture in your mind of exactly where that shot is going. I don't mean you have to drift into a Zen-like trance as you visualize every shot. I simply mean you should know exactly what you are aiming at. Keep the target in your "mind's eye" throughout the entire swing.

Aiming:

The aiming process begins as you approach the ball from behind. Approaching from the side, as many golfers do, does not allow you to form a clear picture of your target in your mind. Once you have picked a target, go through a brief, focused pre-shot routine, then let the shot fly.

Decisiveness:

Decisiveness is a defining trait of the Super Power Golfer. Golfers who cannot make up their minds about where to aim the ball, or with which club to hit the shot, are seldom successful. Make quick, clear decisions, then focus on the target and assume that the ball will end up exactly where you are aiming it.

Michael's comment: There are two prevalent traits I have noticed that all great golfers have: 1) excellent hand-eye coordination, and 2) unshakable concentration. Regarding the former, they are adept not only at striking the ball with great precision, but they seem able to judge exact distances and translate what their eyes are seeing into a physical manifestation; in other words, they can turn something they see into something they do. They seem able to momentarily shut out all distractions while they are first visualizing, then executing their shots.

Dr. King once told me about a concept called "anchoring." He explained that it is a technique used in psychology, specifically during hypnosis. "Anchoring" means teaching oneself, through repetition, one small event, object or occurrence that, when engaged, triggers a chain of following events culminating in a desired result. This works!

Dr. King points out that downhill skiers have long used this technique. When we see them sliding back and forth getting ready for the push down the slope, they are anchoring. "The beeping of the clock as it counts down is the anchor for their start," he says. "The are not talking during this time; rather, they are concentrating intensely on the explosiveness of their start. The golf swing can be viewed as an explosive event that is momentarily all-encompassing."

An excellent anchor for golfers occurs when the club is gripped. Some players are even more specific; they touch the top of the grip with one of their fingers to set their physical and mental powers of concentration into motion. They then visualize the impending golf shot in its entirety, complete with all possible detail.

"The sound, the ball flight, the landing of the ball; the more realistic the visualization, the better the results will be," says Dr. King. "Researchers in London have determined that 80 percent of muscular activity can be perfected by visualization of the task. Try this method. Grip the club, stop talking, start focusing. Visualize the shot in full detail. Assume your stance, strike the ball, follow through. The ball flies to the target, just as you pictured it would. The trance is broken. You're back in the 'real world.'"

The intense concentration of "anchoring" is required for only very short periods of time, perhaps 10-15 seconds just before each shot. This makes it a great technique because it is effective, yet enables you to spend the majority of your time enjoying your surroundings, the scenery, and the companionship and shotmaking of your playing partners.

What drills can increase a golfer's power?

There are many drills you can do to increase your golf swing power. Here are seven of my favorites:

1. Practice hitting balls out of deep grass.

Concentrate on using your legs; a late release will be necessary to get the ball up and out. The resistance provided by the tall grass will help strengthen the wrists and forearms. This is a highly effective drill for increasing the forcefulness of your shots.

2. Hit balls while gripping the club with your right hand only.

You will find that you must turn your body towards the target and keep your wrist firm in order to contact the ball. This drill is a good test of your hand-eye coordination. Expect to "fan the breeze" a few times before you start making solid contact. Many professional golfers have such great hand-eye coordination that they can smack balls almost as far with one hand as they can with both hands.

3. Swing a club in soft sand.

Take a sand divot two or three inches deep. By the way, if the wind is blowing, make sure you are swinging in a downwind direction. A face full of sand will surely be the result should you try it the other way.

4. Make practice swings using a weighted club.

The club's total weight should be 2-3 pounds. The heavy club encourages a late release, helps stretch the upper back and shoulder muscles, and develops the forearms. Weighted clubs are available at many golf stores, as are weighted "donuts" that slip on and off your club. Note: Remember that swinging two or three clubs simultaneously to warm up, or as a strengthening exercise, is not recommended. Gripping multiple clubs while swinging is much different than gripping one club; it can easily throw off your timing and "feel."

5. While standing shoulder-deep in a swimming pool, pretend to swing a club.

Make sure the back of your left hand faces the "target line." The water provides even resistance in all directions. Your hands should remain underwater during the entire swing motion. This is a good way to strengthen your release.

6. "Squeeze and Relax" drill.

Address a ball on the driving range. Just before you swing, squeeze the grip of the club as hard as you can; then relax your hands and make a free-wheeling swing. Swing as hard and fast as you want. Often this drill will result in titanic tee shots, because by squeezing the grip hard, then relaxing and immediately swinging, you release the tension from your hands and arms and really "let it all hang out" with the resulting swing.

7. Hit balls with your feet together.

This drill is especially helpful for golfers who are plagued by a weak slice. Many golfers to whom I show this drill immediately begin to draw, or even hook, the ball. This is because when you hit a golf ball with your feet together you are forced to maintain your balance as you swing your arms past your body; if you do not do these things you literally might fall on your face.

After hitting balls in this manner for a few minutes, spread your feet to normal width and hit a few more shots with your normal path, ball contact, and ball flight.

Hitting balls with my feet together has been the one drill that has helped my golf game the most. Many benefits are derived from this drill. In addition to helping develop balance and tempo in your swing, it also greatly improves hand-eye coordination. Perhaps the biggest contribution this drill made to my game was that it taught me how to hit a variety of shots from 100 yards and in.

Using a variety of clubs - everything from a 6-iron to a sand wedge - I will stand with my feet together and aim at the 100-yard sign on the driving range. After a few minutes I will move to 75-yard shots, then 50-yard shots, then 25-yard shots. Believe me, this drill will help you develop an entire arsenal of shots; it was only after I discovered the feet-together drill that I learned how to hit three-quarter wedge shots and half-wedge shots with confidence.

It is amazing how much you can improve your long game by hitting balls this way. I found that I could drive the ball 200 yards by making smooth swings with my feet together. Indeed, this is my favorite way to practice. A final added benefit is that, since feet-together swings are usually nice and s-m-o-o-t-h, this type of practice is not at all hard on the back in the way that hitting a lot of balls with a full, hard swing can be.

How should a practice schedule be arranged?

A practice schedule, of course, must be based on each individual golfer's needs. Some golfers, such as Bruce Lietzke, do not practice at all and play quite well. Others, like Vijay Singh, hit many dozens of practice balls each day. For most accomplished golfers, 60-80% of practice time is devoted to the short game. Davis Love, for example, stepped up his game a notch or two once he began following this strategy. On the other side of the coin, Lee Trevino at one point in his career was hitting 1000 balls per day on the practice range. He did this to teach himself to hit a controlled fade rather than the erratic draw/hook that was making it hard for him to earn a living as a struggling first-year tour player.

Personally, I believe that the average golfer will benefit much more from practicing chipping and putting than from spending endless hours beating balls on the range, particularly if the golfer does not have sound swing mechanics. After all, it does little good to spend hour after hour on the range grooving one's "bad" habits. Once a golfer has learned a simple, fundamentally sound swing and can consistently hit adequate drives, chipping and putting should encompass a major portion of practice time.

A weekly practice schedule:

The following is a simple model for setting up a weekly practice schedule. This model demonstrates an example of a weekly schedule during which you are performing two physical training workouts per week, in addition to your golf practice and golf-playing sessions.

You should adapt this model to your own needs; it can be structured to fit the Off-Season, Pre-Season, and golf-Season workout schedules presented in chapter 2. Alternate days that are devoted mostly to physical training with days when you mainly play and practice golf.

DAY 1:	A.M.:	First workout of the week.
	P.M.:	Practice swings with feet together.
		Practice pre-shot routine.
DAY 2:	A.M.:	Make practice swings in heavy rough.
		Practice wedges and short irons.
	P.M.:	Practice putting.
DAY 3:	A.M.:	Practice chipping.
		Practice bunker shots.
	P.M.:	Mentally rehearse your next round of golf.

DAY 4:	A.M.:	Second workout of the week.
	P.M.:	Hit balls with feet together. Practice middle irons and long irons.
DAY 5:	A.M.:	Work on weak points of game.
	P.M.:	Practice putting.
DAY 6:	A.M.:	Hit balls with right hand only. Practice driver and fairway woods.
	P.M.:	Practice chipping and pitching. Practice trouble shots.
DAY 7:	A.M.:	Play golf.
	P.M.:	Work on weak points of game.

Remember, adapt the above model to fit your own needs, structuring it to fit the Pre-Season, Off-Season, and Golf-Season segments presented in chapter 2.

Wild abandon:

A final word: One way to inject power into your game is to dedicate the occasional round of golf entirely to the power philosophy. Don't worry about your score, just play with wild abandon. Try to smash every tee ball 300 yards. Fire right at the pin on all your iron shots. On and around the greens, try to sink every chip and every putt. Putt the ball hard at the back of the hole; hard enough to take all the break out of the putt. It is immensely satisfying to play a round of golf in this manner, and you'll be amazed at how many heroic shots you can pull off when you're not worried about your score. You'll build confidence in your arsenal of power, a confidence that will breed success in all areas of your game!

7: Questions And Answers

Weight training:

Q. What causes muscle soreness? Should I work out if I am still extremely sore from the previous workout?

A. Muscle soreness can be divided into two categories: 1) acute soreness, and, 2) delayed soreness. Acute soreness occurs during training, and is most likely caused by an accumulation of "waste" products in the muscle cells due to a lack of blood flow to the muscle during intense contractions. Delayed soreness occurs 12 to 48 hours after training, and is most likely caused by trauma to connective tissues such as tendons and ligaments. Should you be extremely sore from your previous workout, it is a good idea not to train until the soreness is mostly gone. The reason: a golfer's weight training program is most effective when performed at a level that allows an improvement over the previous workout. If you are so sore that your performance suffers, then there is no point in doing the workout. Do not be afraid to wait an extra day or two if your muscles are extremely sore. If waiting allows you to perform better, then waiting is a smart choice.

Q. The Super Power Golfer weight training program calls for four basic weight training movements: the Deadlift, Leg Press, Bench Press and Pulldown. Is it acceptable for me to substitute other exercises; for example, could I substitute an overhead pressing movement for the bench press, or the barbell squat exercise for leg presses?

A. It is acceptable to substitute other movements, particularly if you are experienced at weight training. The four basic movements presented in this book, however, are among the best for golfers. Using your specific examples to illustrate: The overhead press in an effective movement; we have, however, chosen to present it not as a weight training movement, but as a conditioning movement (the "Squat-Press") in chapter 4. We made this choice because we prefer prefer the overhead press as a lightweight, high-repetition movement.

The barbell squat movement, pictured at right, is a great bodybuilding exercise, but for golfers it holds no advantage over the leg press. The squat tends to put the lower back region at risk, and can sometimes be hard on the knee joints. The leg press is a safer choice, and just as effective as the squat for a golfer looking to build lower body power. It should also be noted that the Deadlift exercise is essentially the same movement as the squat, the only difference being the position of the weights. In the Deadlift the weights are held in the hands, with the arms hanging straight down, while in a barbell squat the weights are supported across the rear of the shoulders. The two exercises, because they are so similar, work the same muscles in almost identical fashion; it is therefore not necessary to include them both in a golfer's program.

Q. Is the old-style "full sit-up" a good exercise for the abdominal muscles?

A. The only problem with performing a "full" sit-up motion, wherein you would "sit up" until your upper body is perpendicular to the floor (as opposed to the "crunch" movement, which entails a much shorter range of motion), is that the abdominals do not do all the work. When you do a full sit-up, the powerful hip flexor muscles are engaged and tend to receive the majority of the overload from the exercise. Also, full sit-ups have been associated with lower back strain in some cases particularly when the trainee leans too far forward at the top of the movement. Again, the crunch movement is highly effective and inherently safe, which makes it the better choice for golfers.

Q. Is it more effective to perform Abdominal Crunches and Reverse Crunches on an inclined sit-up board where the feet are anchored at a level higher than the head?

A. No; in fact, the opposite might be true. Many trainees have found that performing these movements at a decline (head higher than the feet) angle maximizes leverage and allows better form and a stronger, more effective muscular contraction. Pictured below are the Abdominal Crunch and Reverse Crunch performed in such a fashion.

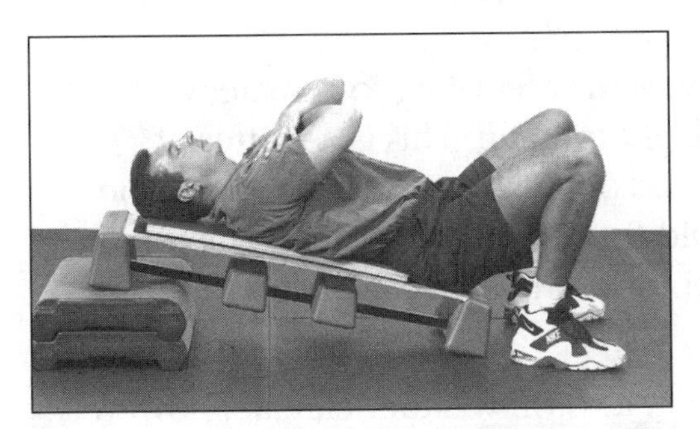

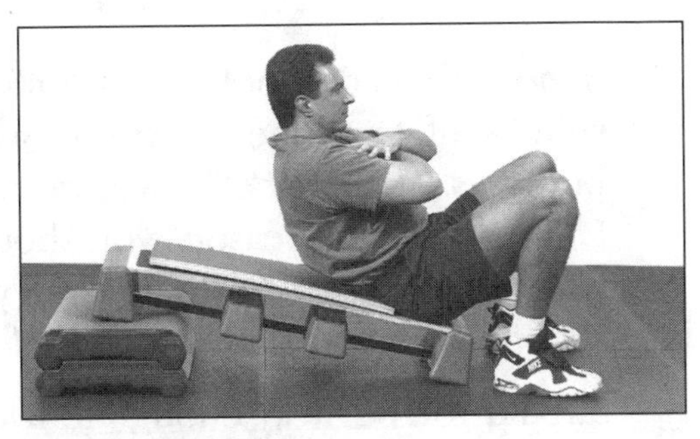

Decline Abdominal Crunch.

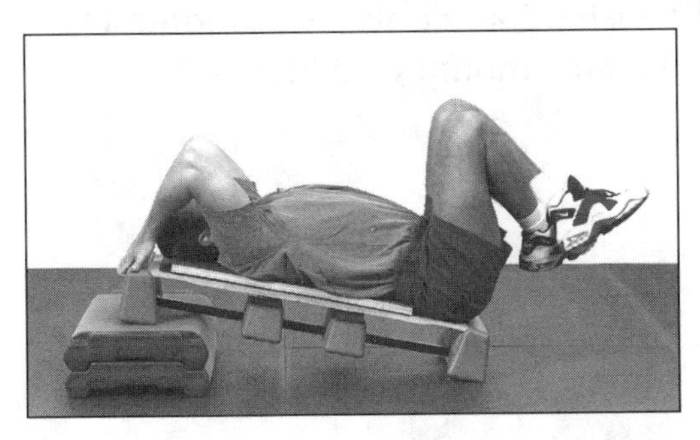

Decline Reverse Crunch.

Training routines and schedules:

Q. Is it O.K. to lift weights and play golf on the same day?

A. This would be entirely an individual matter. In general, most golfers would probably have a difficult time playing at peak form immediately after an intense workout, but some golfers may actually play better because the fatigue from working out might force them to swing more smoothly. There is only one way to find out which category you fall into: pump iron, then hit the links!

Q. I live in a warm climate and play golf three times per week all year round; thus, I do not have an "Off-Season" per se. How does this affect the way I schedule my workouts over the course of the year?

A. Although you do not have an "Off-Season" according to climate, you should still have one in terms of weight training. This is a matter of priorities. The most effective way to accomplish any goal is to focus on it. During your "Off-Season" you should make weight training your priority; when "Golf Season" rolls around, your foremost thought should be shooting the lowest scores possible.

Should you be lucky enough to live in a warm-weather climate, however, it is permissible to alter the duration of your Off-Season, Pre-Season and Golf Season. For example, you might wish to have only a two month Off-Season, a one-month Pre-Season, and a nine-month Golf Season.

Stretching, flexibility and warming up:

Q. I have never stretched in my life, yet I have a good golf swing and play to a one-handicap. Furthermore, I do not usually warm up before I play, yet I do not feel that my performance suffers. Is it really necessary for me to stretch and warm up?

A. It is important to remember that an excessive level of flexibility is not a necessity for a golfer; what is required is adequate flexibility. If you have a sound golf swing and play to a high level, stretching may not be a requirement for you. A sound warm-up, however, can benefit everyone. Who knows, if you warmed up faithfully and regularly you might play to a plus one handicap!

Aerobic exercise:

Q. Should I drink water during aerobic exercise?

A. You should drink water before, during, and after aerobic exercise. It is crucial to keep the human body well hydrated at all times. Drinking water, for that matter, is also a good idea before, during and after a round of golf. This applies in cold weather as well as warm and hot weather; it is surprisingly easy to become dehydrated in weather of all types.

Q. My doctor advised me to monitor my heart rate during exercise. How should I do this, why is it important, and how fast should my heart be beating during exercise?

A. You can monitor your heart rate either manually or through the use of a heart rate monitor. Should you choose to do it manually, place the index finger and middle finger of one hand lightly on either your wrist area just below the thumb pad, or the carotid artery on either side of your neck. Feel for your pulse. Count the beats-per-minute for ten seconds and multiply by six to calculate your heart rate. For example, if you count 20 beats in a ten-second period, your heart rate is 120 beats-per-minute (20 multiplied by 6).

A heart rate monitor is comprised of a wireless transmitter worn around the chest area and a wristwatch receiver worn on the wrist. The receiver automatically displays your heart rate.

It is important to know your heart rate because it helps you stay in a "target zone" wherein you are maximizing the health and fitness benefits of aerobic exercise. Your target zone is usually defined as being between 60% and 90% of your maximum heart rate.

Your maximum heart rate is the theoretical upper limit of how fast your heart can beat while exercising. Maximum heart rate may be calculated by subtracting your age from 220. A 40-year-old man, for example, would have a maximum heart rate of 180 (220 minus 40). This man's target zone would be between 108 beats per minute (60% of 180) and 162 (90% of 180).

If you are just beginning an exercise program, or you have a subpar level of cardiovascular conditioning, stay close to the 60% level of maximum heart rate. Only those athletes who are highly conditioned should venture into the 90% range.

Common golf-related injuries:

Q. I have a "rotator cuff" injury that simply will not go away. A friend advised me that arthroscopic surgery could permanently cure my shoulder pain. Is this type of surgery a viable option?

A. Surgery should always be the last resort in the treatment of any injury. Most sports medicine practitioners currently employ a conservative "rest and exercise" approach to treating shoulder problems. Stretching, resistance training, and mobility exercises form the core of this approach.

While it is true that a small percentage of shoulder-injury patients may eventually require surgery, in the vast majority of cases surgery will not be required. The human body has a remarkable ability to heal itself if given enough time and a proper protocol. find a reputable sports medicine doctor, follow his advice, and consider the option of surgery to be your last resort.

Q. Is it ever advisable to apply heat (rather than ice) to an injured area?

A. Most injuries involve trauma and swelling in the affected area. Ice promotes healing and reduces swelling; heat does not. Ice, therefore, is almost always the treatment of choice. One possible exception is the use of heat treatment to treat an arthritic condition in cold weather. Other than that, ice it!

Q. Is there any difference in the types of golf-related injuries typically suffered by female golfers as opposed to male golfers?

A. Female golfers, perhaps because they often have trouble releasing the hands and wrist during the swing, often seem to suffer injuries to the elbow, hand, and wrist areas. Male golfers tend to have a greater proportion of lower back problems, perhaps because they tend to overswing and try to hit the ball too hard.

Women usually benefit greatly from "clubhead release" drills such as "swinging through tall grass," as described by Tom Stevenson in chapter 6. Male golfers should avoid low back woes by strengthening the abdominal and low back musculature.

Q. What is the difference between the "broomstick exercise" and "rotating with a golf club across the shoulders?" They seem to be very similar movements. Why is the "broomstick exercise" considered a good exercise, while "rotating" is a bad exercise?

A. Although these movements may look the same, in reality they are not similar. The "broomstick" exercise closely mimics an actual golf swing; the hips turn through in a natural fashion and there is little or no negative stress on the vertebra and discs of the spine. conversely, "rotating with a club across the shoulders" does not allow the hips to achieve a natural motion. "Rotating" in this fashion does not mimic a real golf swing; thus, it is not considered to be a beneficial movement.

The power golf swing:

Q. Should taller golfers use longer clubs? Will extra-long clubs generate more power for a shorter golfer?

A. The answer on both counts is "not necessarily." The percentage of golfers who need extra-long clubs is surprisingly small. A golfer who is taller than normal, for example, may also have longer-than-normal-length arms. There is no reason, therefore, that he should need extra-long clubs.

As for a shorter golfer generating more power with extra-long clubs, well, remember that the single most important factor in producing power is clubhead speed at impact. If the golfer in question can produce a well-timed hit with high clubhead speed at impact with a longer club, then, yes, more power will result. Quite often, however, the longer club will make it more difficult to time the hit and more difficult to maintain clubhead speed. Less power becomes the result in that case.

Have a reliable club-fitting professional help you determine whether or not you need longer-than-normal clubs. The most likely scenario is that standard length clubs will do the job for you quite nicely.

Q. Is a right-to left (draw) shot inherently more powerful than a left-to-right (fade) shot?

A. Jack Nicklaus has almost always hit a fade. So do scores of other powerful golfers. Don't worry about whether your predominant shot is right-to-left or left-to-right. Which way the ball curves in the air on its way to its destination is of little importance. Just smack it with SUPER power and enjoy the game!

"If it ain't the

U.S. Open,

then don't bother

playing it safe."

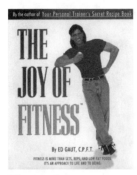

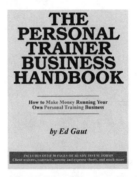